Table of Contents

Part 1
Grammar, Usage, and Mechanics

Unit 1 The Sentence

Unit 2 Nouns

Unit 3 Verbs

Unit 4 Adjectives

Unit 5 Capitalization and Punctuation

Unit 6 Pronouns

Name ____________________

1 What Is a Sentence?

Sentences	Band music is very popular with people of all ages. People have listened to bands for hundreds of years.
Sentence fragments	Band music. Is very popular with people of all ages. For hundreds of years.

A Write *S* after each group of words that is a sentence. Write *F* after each group of words that is a sentence fragment.

1. John Philip Sousa was a famous bandleader. ____

   From 1854 to 1932. ____

2. Sousa was born in Washington, D.C. ____

   Visited many places around the world. ____

3. More than one hundred marches. ____

   Sousa wrote music. ____

4. You probably know some of his music. ____

   "The Stars and Stripes Forever." ____

B **5–10.** This concert announcement has six sentences and several sentence fragments. Underline the sentences.

Example: Hear Sousa's marches on CD.
"Stars and Stripes" the best.

Proofreading Marks
- ¶ Indent
- ∧ Add
- ℘ Delete
- ≡ Capital letter
- / Small letter

Proofreading

Hear our award-winning marching band play tonight at 8:00 p.m. Back from the state band competition. Fifth Street School auditorium. Tickets will be sold at the door. Come early. Seats limited. There will be music for everyone to enjoy. Music of John Philip Sousa. Our band is the State Middle School Marching Band Champion. Get ready to march!

(continued)

Name ______________________________

1 What Is a Sentence? *(continued from page 1)*

Challenge

Find the five complete sentences below. Write the sentences in order on the lines. Then circle the first letter of each sentence. The letters you circle will spell the name of something that is important in a band.

1. Several kinds of bands.
2. Dance bands are popular.
3. On records or on tape.
4. Radios play band music.
5. Usually people like bands.
6. Once in a while a loud noise.
7. Playing in a band.
8. Many students like Sousa's music.
9. Trying to play like John Philip Sousa.
10. Sousa wrote a book about his life.

____

____

____

____

____

Writing Application: A Music Review

EXPLAINING

Think about a record that you like. Write five sentences telling why you like it. Make sure that your sentences are complete.

Name ______________________________

2 Four Kinds of Sentences

Declarative sentence	There are many ways of sending messages.
Interrogative sentence	How many ways do you know?
Imperative sentence	Take this note to your mother.
Exclamatory sentence	What a strange message this is!

A Write the correct end punctuation for each sentence. Then label each sentence *declarative, interrogative, imperative,* or *exclamatory*.

1. Have you ever received a telegram ____ ____________
2. How exciting it is ____ ____________
3. Telegrams were popular before we had telephones ____ ____________
4. Do you know who invented the telegraph ____ ____________
5. Read about it here ____ ____________
6. Samuel F. B. Morse was one of the inventors ____ ____________
7. What a clever person he was ____ ____________
8. He also invented Morse code ____ ____________

B **9–15.** Use proofreading marks to add or correct seven end punctuation marks in this telegram.

Example: Do you think I should send a telegram?

Proofreading Marks

- ¶ Indent
- ∧ Add
- Delete
- ≡ Capital letter
- / Small letter

Marcus,

What exciting news we have for you Your sister Tanya had twins! They were born yesterday You have a new niece and a new nephew I can't believe it.

Your sister and the babies are fine? Can you come home to see them soon. Remember to send a card to your sister

(continued)

Name ____________________

2 Four Kinds of Sentences *(continued from page 3)*

Challenge

The students in Mr. Novak's class wanted to make the invitations to their party sound like telegrams. Instead of using end punctuation, they ended every sentence with the word *STOP*. Rewrite the invitation on the lines below. Replace each *STOP* with the correct end punctuation.

TELEGRAM

We are having a party Thursday afternoon STOP Can you come STOP It will be such fun STOP Bring this invitation with you STOP Present it at the door STOP

Mr. Novak's class

Now underline the first word in each imperative sentence you have written. The words form a hidden message. Write the message here.

____

Writing Application: A Message

INFORMING

You have been shipwrecked on an island in the middle of the ocean. You find a piece of paper, a pencil, and a bottle. Write a message to put into the bottle. Your message must include one declarative sentence, one interrogative sentence, one imperative sentence, and one exclamatory sentence.

Grade 5: Unit 1 The Sentence *(Use with pupil book pages 34–35.)*
Skill: Students will write and punctuate the four kinds of sentences.

Name ______________________________

3 Subjects and Predicates

Complete Subjects	Complete Predicates
A group of students	learned many new facts.
Weights and measures	fascinated them.

Underline each complete subject once. Underline each complete predicate twice.

1. The boys and girls studied different kinds of measures.
2. Some people of ancient times used cubits.
3. A cubit measured about twenty inches.
4. It was the distance from the elbow to the tip of the middle finger.
5. Ancient people based other units on body measurements.
6. Romans used the uncia as a unit of measurement.
7. The uncia was equivalent to the width of a person's thumb.
8. Twelve uncia equaled the length of a person's foot.
9. The differences in people's sizes made this system inaccurate.
10. The system failed because of this.
11. Modern systems of measurement are more exact.
12. The students wrote reports on modern measurement.
13. Mark and Nadia read about furlongs.
14. A furlong equals one-eighth of a mile.
15. Many of the students learned about nautical miles.
16. Nautical miles are longer than land miles.
17. A nautical mile equals about 6,076 feet.
18. We call the speed of one nautical mile per hour a knot.
19. Modern ships and some planes report their speed in knots.
20. The sailors and pilots use knots in navigation as well.

(continued)

Name ______________________________

3 Subjects and Predicates *(continued from page 5)*

Challenge

Draw a line between the complete subject and the complete predicate of each sentence.

1. The metric system is a group of units.
   1 1
2. These units measure length, temperature, or weight.
   2 2
3. Scientists created the metric system.
   3 3
4. They made the system logical and exact.
   4 4
5. Nonscientists can learn the system easily.
   5 5
6. No other system of measurement is as simple as the metric system.
   6 6
7. People use the metric system in many countries.
   7 7
8. The term *metric* comes from the system's basic unit of length.
   8 8
9. This basic unit of length is the meter.
   9 9
10. A meter is slightly longer than a yard.
    10 10

Now look at the complete predicates. Write the numbered letters from the complete predicates in the boxes below.

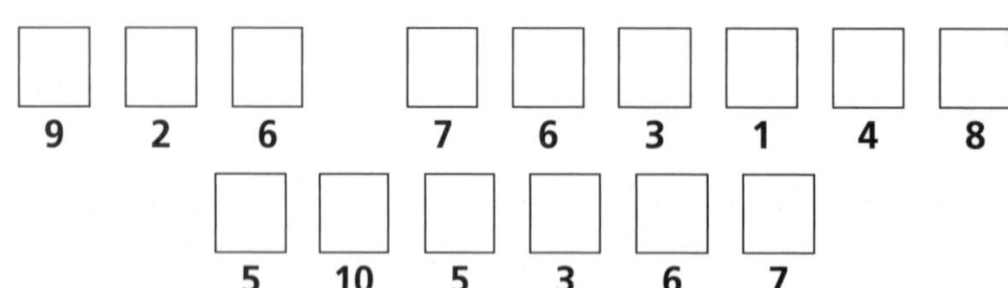

9 2 6 7 6 3 1 4 8

5 10 5 3 6 7

Writing Application: A Ship's Report

You are a navigator on a ship. Write five sentences to the captain, telling about the speed and direction of the ship. Draw a line between the complete subject and the complete predicate of each sentence.

Grade 5: Unit 1 The Sentence *(Use with pupil book pages 36–37.)*
Skill: Students will identify complete subjects and complete predicates.

Name ______________________________

4 Simple Subjects

My older **cousin** from Houston traveled to Florida.
The **Florida Everglades** was her first stop.
She loved seeing the wildlife.
The park's **beauty** impressed her.

Write the simple subject of each sentence.

1. Maria is my cousin. ______________
2. She went on a trip to Florida last summer. ______________
3. Maria's trip was interesting. ______________
4. Her family visited Everglades National Park. ______________
5. Everglades National Park is mostly swamps. ______________
6. A large part of the park is underwater. ______________
7. It contains many types of plants. ______________
8. Some plants grow as high as seventy feet! ______________
9. Many animals live there. ______________
10. The park is known for its amphibian population. ______________
11. Some birds stay there for the winter. ______________
12. They fly north for the summer. ______________
13. The birds' routes have been traced. ______________
14. Visitors to the Everglades can see the routes. ______________
15. There are many freshwater and saltwater areas in the Everglades. ______________
16. Its subtropical wilderness is the largest in the continental United States. ______________
17. So many flowers dot the Everglades landscape. ______________
18. Many kinds of orchids bring color to the park. ______________

(continued)

Name ______________________________

4 Simple Subjects *(continued from page 7)*

Challenge

Underline the simple subject of each sentence.

1. Beautiful plants grow in the Everglades.
2. The sun often shines brightly.
3. Fish swim in the water.
4. Some plants provide shelter for the fish.
5. The fish in the Everglades are interesting.
6. Some fish are found only in warm waters.
7. Birds in the Everglades include wild turkeys and wading birds.
8. Most fish try to hide from the birds.
9. The large, fierce alligators do not fear the birds.
10. The birds flee from alligators.

Now complete this Everglades food chain. Write the simple subjects in the numbered blanks below.

______ (1) make food from the ______ (2).

Little ______ (3) eat ______ (4).

Big ______ (5) eat little ______ (6).

Some ______ (7) eat big ______ (8).

______ (9) eat some ______ (10).

Writing Application: A Journal

DESCRIBING

You are spending five days in the land of Zog. There are beautiful plants and strange animals. Each day you see something new and different. Write a sentence for each day, describing a sight you have seen. Underline the simple subject of each sentence.

Name ______________________

5 Simple Predicates

Felicia **learned** about insects.
She **has discovered** many interesting facts.

Write the simple predicate of each sentence.

1. Most people find cockroaches troublesome. ____________
2. These household pests get into everything. ____________
3. The history of these pests may surprise you. ____________
4. These insects are strange and amazing creatures. ____________
5. The cockroach family might be 300 million years old! ____________
6. A roach's antennae discover tiny amounts of water. ____________
7. Four mouth feelers search for food. ____________
8. Bristles cover its strong legs. ____________
9. Its legs make it one of the world's fastest insects. ____________
10. A baby roach grows into an adult in ten weeks. ____________
11. Over 3,500 kinds of roaches exist all over the world. ____________
12. Some scientists study cockroaches and other insects. ____________
13. Such scientists are called entomologists. ____________
14. The scientists have learned respect for the insects. ____________
15. The cockroach is a genius at survival. ____________
16. It adapts easily to any environment. ____________
17. Many other tiny creatures interest humans. ____________
18. You will read about one of them on the next page. ____________

(continued)

Name ______________________________

5 Simple Predicates *(continued from page 9)*

Challenge

Underline the simple predicate of each sentence below.

1. Hundreds or even thousands of these insects live together in colonies.
2. Some colonies have made mounds up to forty feet high!
3. The mounds contain homes for the insects.
4. Most of the insects are workers or soldiers.
5. These insects eat wood.
6. The insects damage property.
7. The insects' bodies can turn wood into food.
8. They have destroyed some buildings.

Now write the simple predicates in order on the lines below. Then follow the directions next to each line.

1. ______________________ Circle the second letter.
2. ______________________ Circle the fourth letter.
3. ______________________ Circle the fourth letter.
4. ______________________ Circle the second letter.
5. ______________________ Circle the first letter.
6. ______________________ Circle the third letter.
7. ______________________ Circle the fourth letter.
8. ______________________ Circle the seventh letter.

Unscramble the circled letters to spell the name of the insect discussed in the sentences above.

These insects are ______________________ .

Writing Application: A Description

Write five sentences about your life as if you were an insect. Underline each simple predicate.

Name ______________________________

6 Subjects in Imperatives

Declarative sentence	**Joshua** mashed the potatoes.
Imperative sentence	***(You)*** Mash the potatoes, please.

For each sentence, write *D* for declarative or *I* for imperative. Then write the simple subject of the sentence.

1. Potatoes are an ancient crop. ______ ______________
2. Tell me more about potatoes. ______ ______________
3. We eat the underground stem. ______ ______________
4. Please give me some more facts. ______ ______________
5. The vegetables first grew in South America. ______ ______________
6. Spanish explorers took them to Europe. ______ ______________
7. Please explain how they were grown. ______ ______________
8. The Inca grew them in the mountains. ______ ______________
9. They used potatoes to make a special flour. ______ ______________
10. Guess how the flour was made. ______ ______________
11. Let me think, please. ______ ______________
12. Show me how it was done. ______ ______________
13. The Inca mashed the potatoes with their feet. ______ ______________
14. Imagine walking on all those potatoes. ______ ______________
15. People still make potato flour today. ______ ______________
16. Please don't ask me to do the mashing. ______ ______________
17. The English people did not eat potatoes until the eighteenth century. ______ ______________
18. Guess why that happened. ______ ______________
19. Tell me why the Irish grew potatoes. ______ ______________
20. The potato may be used for food in space. ______ ______________

(continued)

Name ______________________

6 Subjects in Imperatives (continued from page 11)

Challenge

Complete this television advertisement for Tater Potatoes. Write an imperative sentence under each television screen to tell what each announcement is saying.

1.

____

____

3.

____

____

2.

____

____

4.

____

____

Now make up your own advertisement for a new kind of food. Draw your advertisement on another piece of paper.

Writing Application: Directions

You have invented a new way of cooking potatoes. Write five or more sentences explaining your method. Include three imperative sentences. List the simple subject for each sentence you write.

Name ______________________

7 Conjunctions

Scientists **and** other people use thermometers.
Thermometers can indicate a fever, **but** they cannot cure it.
They can measure warm weather **or** indicate cold weather.

Complete each sentence. Write the conjunction that has the meaning given in parentheses.

1. The Fahrenheit ________ the Celsius are scales. **(joins together)**
2. Many people in the United States use Fahrenheit thermometers, ________ in Canada the Celsius scale is used. **(shows contrast)**
3. Do you use a Fahrenheit thermometer, ________ do you prefer a Celsius thermometer? **(shows choice)**
4. The two thermometers measure the same things ________ do this in different ways. **(shows contrast)**
5. On the Fahrenheit scale, water freezes at 32 degrees, ________ on the Celsius scale, it freezes at 0 degrees. **(shows contrast)**
6. The temperature of boiling water is 212 degrees Fahrenheit, ________ it is 100 degrees Celsius. **(shows contrast)**
7. Announcers ________ forecasters use either scale. **(joins together)**
8. They say "Fahrenheit," ________ they say "Celsius" to let you know which one they are using. **(shows choice)**
9. Some announcers use ________ report both scales. **(joins together)**
10. Listen to the weather report tomorrow morning ________ find out which thermometer the announcer is using. **(joins together)**

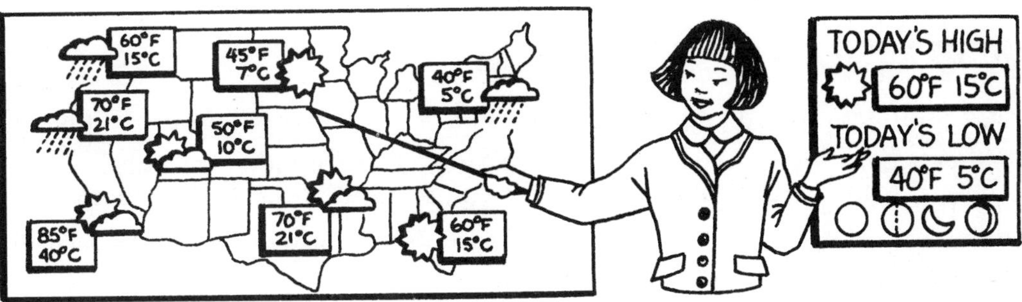

(continued)

Name ______________________________

7 Conjunctions (continued from page 13)

Challenge

The students in Mrs. Pizarro's class made up a game for conjunctions. In their game, *or* is worth 3 points, *but* is worth 2 points, and *and* is worth 1 point. Play the game by completing the following sentences with conjunctions. Write your points on the lines in the thermometer.
WARNING: The conjunction must make sense in the sentence!

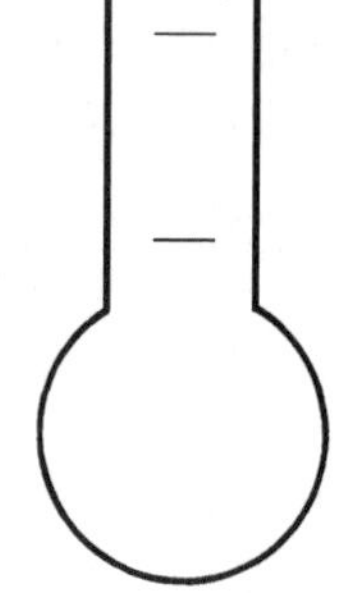

1. Galileo made a thermometer, __________ it was not accurate.
2. The device had a scale __________ was called a thermoscope.
3. The thermometer used water __________ other liquids.
4. The device didn't use alcohol, __________ others did.
5. Did Fahrenheit __________ Celsius first use mercury?
6. The first scales used boiling water, __________ they used melting ice as a fixed temperature.
7. New thermometers use air __________ work by electricity.

Add up your score. How many points did you get? __________

Stump a friend! On a separate sheet of paper, write five sentences in which more than one conjunction can make sense. Leave a blank line for each conjunction. See how many points your friend can get.

Writing Application: A Weather Report

Congratulations! You are going to be on television tonight. You will give the weather report. Write five sentences, telling what the weather will be like tomorrow. Use a conjunction in each sentence.

Name ______________________________

Writing Good Sentences

Two sentences	Whales are adapted for diving. They can stay underwater for up to an hour.
Compound sentence	Whales are adapted for diving, **and** they can stay underwater for up to an hour.

Combining Sentences 1–4. Rewrite these paragraphs from a report. Combine the underlined sentences, using a comma and a conjunction such as *and*, *but*, or *or*.

Revising

Sea mammals are some of the most interesting creatures in the world. Whales are sea mammals. They spend much of their time underwater. They must surface to breathe. Some whales have teeth. Some have powerful, toothless gums. Toothed whales can dive about 3,000 meters. The toothless baleen whale stays near the surface of the sea.

Male whales sing to attract females. The humpback whale is a large baleen whale. It is the best-known whale "singer." You can go on special whaling boats to hear whale sounds, or you can hear recordings of whale "songs."

(continued)

Name ______________________________

Writing Good Sentences *(continued from page 15)*

Stringy sentence	The giraffe walks by moving both right legs and then both left legs and its walk is called an amble.
Separate sentences	The giraffe walks by moving both right legs and then both left legs. Its walk is called an amble.

Avoiding Stringy Sentences 5–8. Break up the four stringy sentences in these picture captions. Write single ideas as short sentences. Use the conjunctions *and, but,* or *or* to write pairs of ideas as compound sentences.

Revising

A species of flying squirrel lives in Africa and is related to the squirrels that you see every day and it does not really fly, it glides.

A kangaroo has thighs, shins, and feet of almost equal length and its tail acts as a counterbalance and it can hop 42 feet in one jump.

The cheetah is the world's fastest sprinter and a cheetah can run about 70 miles an hour and only over short distances.

A dolphin is streamlined for fast swimming and its tail has two flukes and the muscles in the flukes act as a propeller and a rudder.

5. ______________________________

____

6. ______________________________

____

7. ______________________________

____

8. ______________________________

____

Grade 5: Unit 1 The Sentence *(Use with pupil book pages 46–47.)*
Skill: Students will rewrite stringy sentences as short or compound sentences.

Name ______________________________

8 Run-on Sentences

Run-on sentence	Helen lives in Arizona Tanya lives in Alaska.
Correct	Helen lives in Arizona. **T**anya lives in Alaska.
Also correct	Helen lives in Arizona, but Tanya lives in Alaska.

A Correct these run-on sentences. First, separate each one into two sentences. Then write each one as a compound sentence.

1. People dress one way for the cold they dress another way for the heat.

   Separate: ______________________________

   ____

   Compound: ______________________________

   ____

2. Some clothes keep you warm some keep you cool.

   Separate: ______________________________

   ____

   Compound: ______________________________

   ____

B **3–6.** Use proofreading marks to correct four run-on sentences in this weather report.

Example: Wool is warm. cotton is cool.
or
Wool is warm, but cotton is cool.

Proofreading Marks

- ¶ Indent
- ∧ Add
- Delete
- ≡ Capital letter
- / Small letter

Proofreading

Expect rain this morning the sun will come out this afternoon. The high temperature will be in the sixties the low will be in the forties. Some areas will have fog it will clear by the morning. The forecast for the weekend looks great. Sunday will be sunny do something outdoors.

(continued)

Name ______________________________

8 Run-on Sentences *(continued from page 17)*

Challenge

This radio announcer was so excited about a new product that she ran all of her sentences together! Help her by rewriting the advertisement. Correct each run-on sentence.

Thermesh is a new space-age material it is made of special metallic fibers no other fiber is like Thermesh it will keep you warm in the winter it will keep you cool in the summer it never needs ironing it won't crush, tear, or rust Thermesh is waterproof use it as a tent it is soft enough for a baby's blanket you will never find another fabric like Thermesh why should you settle for less this miracle material is not sold in stores supplies are limited don't miss your chance order Thermesh today!

____

____

____

____

____

____

____

____

Writing Application: A Letter

You have just moved to the North Pole. Write a letter to your friend in Florida. Tell your friend about your life. Be sure you do not write any run-on sentences.

Grade 5: Unit 1 The Sentence *(Use with pupil book pages 48–49.)*
Skill: Students will correct run-on sentences.

Name ______________________________

1 What Is a Noun?

Persons	relative	Sara	Uncle Ed
Places	bay	Hudson Bay	Bay of Fundy
Things	games	Olympics	baseball
Ideas	safety	problem	agreement

Write the nouns in each sentence.

1. My aunt works at Woods Hole as a scientist.

____

2. Aunt Jane has an understanding of the habits of whales.

____

3. These mammals spend their entire life in the sea.

____

4. These animals are the largest creatures on Earth.

____

5. Their brains may be as big as watermelons.

____

6. Blue whales measure 30 meters.

____

7. Whales eat the fish that eat plankton.

____

8. Biologists are studying ways to measure their intelligence.

____

9. Some species that have neared extinction are now protected.

____

10. New laws in the United States call for their protection.

____

(continued)

Name ______________________________

1 What Is a Noun? *(continued from page 19)*

Challenge

Below is a map of Blue Bay. Here are some symbols used on the map:

lighthouse dock whale

lifeguard water ship

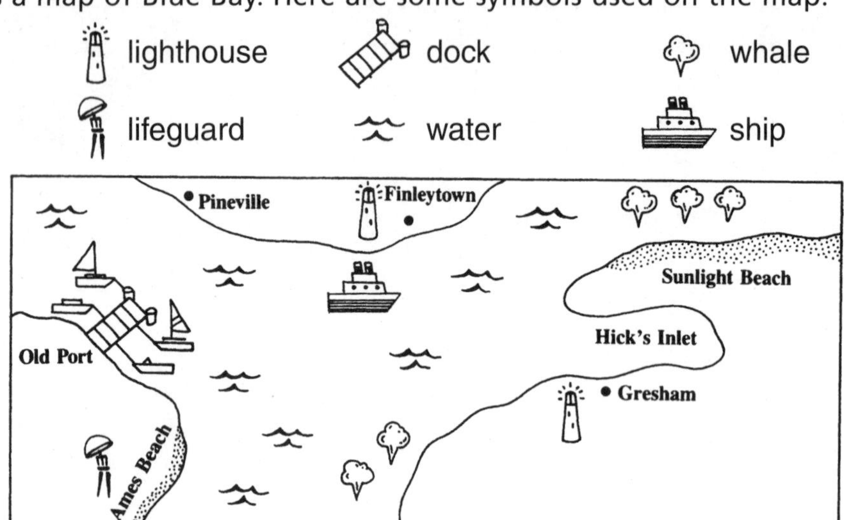

Use the map to find the answers to the questions. Write a complete sentence for each answer. Underline the nouns in your sentences.

1. Where are the two lighthouses?

____

2. Which town is closest to the large ship?

____

3. On which beach is there a lifeguard?

____

4. Where can people keep their boats?

____

Writing Application: A Narrative Report

Suppose that you have suddenly become as big as a whale! Write a paragraph, telling about things you can and cannot do because of your size. Circle each noun in your paragraph.

Name ______________________________

2 Common and Proper Nouns

Common nouns	ranger	place	month	holiday
Proper nouns	Joe Garcia	Grand Canyon	June	Fourth of July

A Underline the nouns in each group of sentences. Then write the proper nouns, using capital letters correctly. The numbers in parentheses tell how many common and proper nouns are in each group of sentences.

1. Last july my family visited banff national park in the province of alberta. banff is among the oldest parks in canada and covers more than 2,500 square miles. **(9)**

____

2. Our group camped near lake louise on the fourth of july and spent two afternoons at the lake. Many special exhibits and informative lectures were offered in the nearby lodge. **(8)**

____

B **3–15.** This post card has thirteen capitalization errors in the names of people, places, and things. Use proofreading marks to correct them.

Example: We visited the blue ridge mountains of virginia in march.

Proofreading

Dear Joe,

My father and I have already visited several states this month. On June 20, dad's friends helena and franco garabis met us in brownsville, texas. They sometimes come across the rio grande river to go shopping in this Country. We all went to a restaurant called rumba. We will also go to padre island.

Proofreading Marks
- ¶ Indent
- ∧ Add
- ⌇ Delete
- ≡ Capital letter
- / Small letter

(continued)

Name ______________________________

2 Common and Proper Nouns (continued from page 21)

Challenge

Look at the meanings of the following symbols. Rewrite the paragraph below. Replace each symbol with the name of a person, a place, or a thing. Capitalize the proper nouns.

a person

a place

a thing

So far the ☆ had gone well. I was proud to be testing my ☆. I got to the [place] and saw the ☆. Now I was getting nervous. Still I wanted the ☆. There was no turning back. [person] and [person] had helped me before. Now it was my turn. I made it to the [place], and there before me was the [place]. I heard a ☆ and then a ☆. What was happening? I turned in time to see the ☆ coming from the [place]. I tried to do something, but my ☆ seemed frozen in fright. Suddenly I heard the voice of the [person] behind me. What a ☆!

____

____

____

____

____

____

Writing Application: A Travel Poster

Make a poster to encourage people to visit your town. Draw a picture of a sight that would interest tourists. Then write five sentences on your poster, explaining why your town is interesting. Underline the common nouns on your poster. Circle the proper nouns.

Name ______________________________

Writing with Nouns

Two sentences	Children enjoy watching television. Adults enjoy watching television.
Combined sentence	Children and adults enjoy watching television.

Combining Sentences: Compound Subjects 1–4. Rewrite these sentences from an entertainment magazine. Combine four pairs of sentences by making compound subjects.

Revising

Television talk shows are very popular. Radio talk shows are very popular. Talk show hosts ask the guests interesting questions. The audience asks questions, too. The studio audience feels as though it is a part of the show. The viewing or listening audience feels the same way. Talk show hosts get to know the "real" people behind the headlines. The audience gets to know them, too.

____

____

____

____

____

____

____

____

____

____

____

____

(continued)

Name ____________________

Writing with Nouns *(continued from page 23)*

Two sentences	Henry Ford was an automotive pioneer. He was one of the first to build a self-propelled vehicle.
Combined sentence	Henry Ford, one of the first to build a self-propelled vehicle, was an automotive pioneer.

Combining Sentences: Telling More About Nouns 5–8. Revise these paragraphs from a book about Henry Ford. Combine each pair of underlined sentences.

Revising

Henry Ford started the Ford Motor Company in 1903. Henry Ford was a 40-year-old businessman from Detroit. The young company produced only a few cars a day. Henry Ford introduced the Model T in 1908. The Model T was a reliable and reasonably priced automobile. So many people wanted to buy his car that he could not make them fast enough.

Then Ford had a new idea for making cars. His idea was the assembly line. The cars moved on belts in a line past workers who each added one part to each car. By the end of the line, the car was complete. The Ford Motor Company sold more cars than ever before. His company was the largest automobile manufacturer in the world.

Grammar

Name ___________________________________

3 Singular and Plural Nouns

Singular Nouns	Plural Nouns	Singular Nouns	Plural Nouns
cat	cat**s**	finch	finch**es**
dove	dove**s**	thrush	thrush**es**
walrus	walrus**es**	donkey	donkey**s**
fox	fox**es**	pony	pon**ies**

If the underlined noun is singular, write the plural form. If it is plural, write the singular form.

1. Aki visited the animals in the zoos. ______________
2. She watched the zebras gallop through the pass. ______________
3. The lynx cared for the baby. ______________
4. The monkey ate the bunch of bananas. ______________
5. Aki heard the crash when the chimp threw a pan. ______________
6. Aki watched the lizards play around the cactus. ______________
7. The parrot was picking the berry from the bush. ______________
8. The jay sat on the perch. ______________
9. The fox slept in the small hutch. ______________
10. Aki told the class about her adventures. ______________

(continued)

Name ______________________________

3 Singular and Plural Nouns *(continued from page 25)*

Challenge

Write a table of contents for a book about animals. The title for each chapter should include the plural form of a noun from the box below. Be sure that each chapter has an interesting title!

jay	walrus	turkey	ostrich	fly
donkey	puppy	guppy	fox	thrush
monkey	bunny	pony	moth	panda

Table of
Contents
page
5
10
17
21
25
32
36
40

Writing Application: A Work Log

You are a zookeeper. Choose five kinds of animals in your zoo and write a sentence, telling what you will feed each of them tomorrow. Use the plural forms of five nouns from the box below.

fox	nuthatch	puppy	skunk
monkey	octopus	rhinoceros	snake

Grade 5: Unit 2 Nouns *(Use with pupil book pages 70–71.)*
Skill: Students will write the plural forms of regular nouns.

Name ______________________________

4 More Plural Nouns

Singular Nouns	Plural Nouns	Singular Nouns	Plural Nouns
leaf	leaves	hero	heroes
giraffe	giraffes	foot	feet
banjo	banjos	deer	deer

A Write the plural form of the noun in parentheses to complete each sentence. You may use your dictionary.

1. Opera lovers can listen to opera on their ______________. **(radio)**
2. Yesterday Murray heard some ______________ sing. **(woman)**
3. They were ______________. **(soprano)**
4. Women with lower voices are called ______________. **(alto)**
5. Some ______________ are tenors, and others are baritones. **(man)**
6. Murray reads about the ______________ of opera stars. **(life)**

B **7–12.** Use proofreading marks to correct this flyer's six errors in plural nouns.

Example: They want to sing the song ~~themselfs~~. themselves

Proofreading Marks
- ¶ Indent
- ∧ Add
- Delete
- ≡ Capital letter
- / Small letter

Proofreading

Parents, Come to Our Concert!

Are you ready to sink your tooths into some serious music? There are still plenty of good seats for our spring and summer concert serieses. We will sing songs to make your foots tap. Latoya Brown and Tino Genedetti will sing soloes. Yari Mehta and Lin Li will accompany us on their viola.

We are also selling concert audiotapes. Look for tapes on the shelfs outside the music studio.

(continued)

Name ______________________________

4 More Plural Nouns *(continued from page 27)*

Challenge

Fabia Howl is writing rhyming word pairs for her new operetta. You can help her by combining the syllables in the notes below to form nouns. Write the plural form of each noun next to its definition.

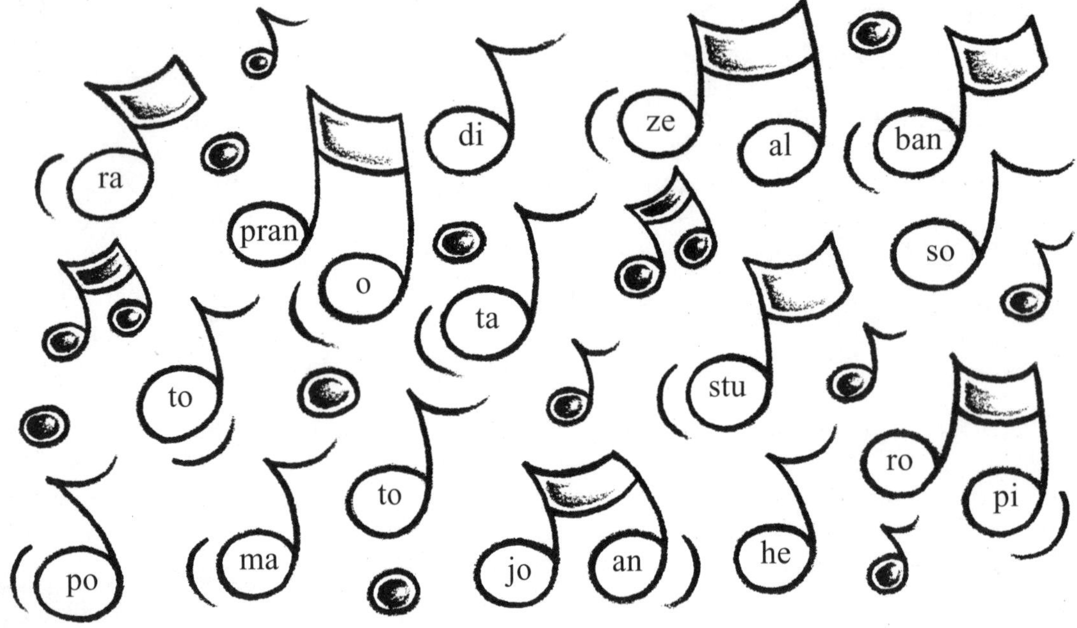

1. vegetables ______________, reddish fruits ______________
2. singers ______________, singers ______________
3. wireless sets ______________, artists' workrooms ______________
4. brave persons ______________, numbers ______________
5. musical instruments ______________, musical instruments ______________

Writing Application: A Personal Narrative

Write a paragraph about something you do or would like to do in your spare time. Use the plural forms of at least four nouns from the box below.

radio	shelf	banjo	hero	tooth
piano	life	studio	foot	stereo

Name ______________________________

5 Singular Possessive Nouns

Singular nouns	friend	student	Amos
Singular possessive nouns	**friend's** team	**student's** bat	**Amos's** decision

A Rewrite each sentence. Change the underlined group of words to include a singular possessive noun.

1. The book belonging to Amos is about the first African-American baseball player in the major leagues.

____

____

2. The name of this baseball player is Jackie Robinson.

____

3. The book is the autobiography of Robinson.

____

4. The playing of this second baseman attracted attention.

____

B 5–10. This student's speech has six errors in singular possessive nouns. Use proofreading marks to correct the speech.

Example: ~~Bess~~ **Bess's** mother is a big Jackie Robinson fan.

Proofreading Marks

- ¶ Indent
- ∧ Add
- Delete
- ≡ Capital letter
- / Small letter

Proofreading

Jackie Robinson, Baseball Hero

Jackie Robinson is one of baseball greatest heroes. When he played for the Dodgers, he was one of the team best players. His hard work and tremendous skill earned the nation respect. He was voted the National League Most Valuable Player in 1949. Robinson talents won him other awards too. Jackie induction into the Hall of Fame occurred in 1962.

(continued)

Name ______________________________

5 Singular Possessive Nouns *(continued from page 29)*

Challenge

Here is the equipment some students brought with them to play a new game called Jump Fast:

Explain how the students above will play Jump Fast, using the equipment they have with them. Write a possessive noun and another noun in each blank.

Jenny will hit ______________________ with ______________________. The ball will bounce over ______________________. Amos must skip once with ______________________ before Katie catches the ball in ________________.

Now invent another game that can be played with the same equipment. On a separate piece of paper, explain how to play the game. Use singular possessive nouns in your explanation.

Writing Application: A Biographical Narrative

Write a paragraph about a real or an imaginary sports star. Explain why the star is famous. Include four or more singular possessive nouns in your paragraph.

Name ______________________________

6 Plural Possessive Nouns

Plural Nouns	Plural Possessive Nouns
bats	**bats'** wings
ladies	**ladies'** shoes
geese	**geese's** feathers
elk	**elk's** teeth

Rewrite each sentence. Change the underlined group of words to include a plural possessive noun.

1. The names of the Marx brothers were Groucho, Harpo, and Chico.

____

2. The acting of the Marxes was famous.

____

3. The first public appearance the actors had was on the stage.

____

4. The jokes of the men were funny.

____

5. Later, movies by these heroes were popular.

____

6. Perhaps the favorite of the children was Harpo.

____

7. Harpo and Chico played music in the films of these stars.

____

8. The instruments these musicians owned were a harp and a piano.

____

9. The movies of the Marx brothers became models for other comedians.

____

10. The walk of Groucho Marx became most famous.

____

(continued)

Name ______________________________

6 Plural Possessive Nouns *(continued from page 31)*

Challenge

Hilda Highbrow is reviewing a new musical group. Help her write her review. Use the details in the picture to help you write the sentences. Use the word in parentheses and a plural possessive noun in each sentence.

1. (pianos) ______________________________
2. (horns) ______________________________
3. (harps) ______________________________
4. (drums) ______________________________
5. (violins) ______________________________

Writing Application: A Movie Review

Write five sentences about a movie that you have seen. Tell what the stars did. Explain why you did or did not like the movie. Include at least three plural possessive nouns in your review.

Name ______________________________

Writing with Nouns

Two sentences	Most teams wear uniforms. The uniforms show the team colors.
Sentence with a possessive noun	Most teams' uniforms show the team colors.

Combining Sentences: Possessive Nouns 1–4. Rewrite this introduction from a book about games. Combine each pair of underlined sentences, using a possessive noun.

Revising

Do you like to play games? Children from all over the world do too! The goal of this book is to teach you how to play games. The games come from every continent. Many games in this book have been popular for hundreds of years. The games of your great-grandparents are probably included in this book. Each game needs special materials. The materials are listed at the top of the page.

Do you like board games? This book has some classic board games. The board games each have a full-page diagram. This book contains many games. The games can be shared with your friends.

____

____

____

____

____

____

____

____

____

(continued)

Name ______________________________

Writing with Nouns *(continued from page 33)*

Two sentences	We look forward to field games every summer. Field games are camp's most exciting activities.
Combined sentence	We look forward to field games, camp's most exciting activities, every summer.

Combining Sentences: Appositives with Possessive Nouns 5–8. Revise this post card. Combine each set of underlined sentences by changing the sentence with the possessive noun into an appositive.

Revising

Dear Grandma,

Field games started today! I am on the red team! The red team was last year's winning team. Maddie is my favorite counselor. Maddie is the red team's leader.

Each team has a mascot. I get to be the red fox. The red fox is our team's mascot. Allison is on the blue team. Allison is my best friend. Allison is the blue team's mascot. These will be the best field games ever!

Love,
Caitlin

____

____

____

____

____

____

____

____

____

Grade 5: Unit 2 Nouns *(Use with pupil book pages 78–79.)*
Skill: Students will combine sentences using appositives with possessive nouns.

Name ____________________

Using Exact Nouns

The ~~man~~ **actor** came to the front of the stage and spoke.

1–10. Replace each underlined noun in this report about a play with a more exact noun from each pair of words in the word box. Be sure the noun you choose fits the meaning of the sentence. Cross out the weak noun and write the exact noun above it.

theater	studio	canoes	warships
gymnasium	auditorium	commands	rhymes
dress	costume	carpenter	soldier
crown	helmet	bundle	bouquet
sofa	throne	roses	zucchini

Revising

Yesterday we went to a <u>building</u> to see a play. We waited awhile in the big, cold <u>room</u>, but then the curtain went up. There on the stage was a woman in a dazzling <u>outfit</u> with a <u>hat</u> on her head, sitting on a great <u>chair</u>. She was England's Good Queen Bess. England was under attack from Spanish <u>boats</u>, and the queen shouted out <u>words</u> to all around her. In the best scene, Good Queen Bess went to an army camp and asked every <u>person</u> to fight hard for England. At the end, the actress who played the queen received a <u>bunch</u> of <u>flowers</u>.

Name ______________________________

1 Action Verbs

Elizabeth **likes** art.
Yesterday she **created** a beautiful vase.

Write the action verb in each sentence.

1. Elizabeth went to an artist's studio. ____________
2. She watched the artist carefully. ____________
3. Elizabeth envied the potter's ability. ____________
4. Elizabeth started a pottery club at school. ____________
5. A different potter comes each week. ____________
6. The potters instruct the students. ____________
7. Elizabeth follows the instructions carefully. ____________
8. First, she kneads the clay. ____________
9. Then she throws a lump of clay onto the potter's wheel. ____________
10. She slowly turns the heavy wheel with her foot. ____________
11. Elizabeth wets her hands in a bowl of water. ____________
12. Her fingers shape the clay. ____________
13. She forms the clay into a mug. ____________
14. Then she molds a piece of clay into a handle. ____________
15. The students place the mugs in a special oven. ____________
16. The clay bakes in the kiln for several hours. ____________
17. Then the students put glaze on their mugs. ____________
18. Some students paint designs on their work. ____________
19. They return their mugs to the kiln. ____________
20. The students display their work at the art fair. ____________

(continued)

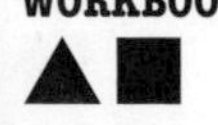

Name ______________________________

1 Action Verbs *(continued from page 36)*

Challenge

The winner of each ticktacktoe game wrote three action verbs in a row. Find out who won each game. First, underline the action verbs in each game. Then write whether "X" or "O" won the game.

X cobra	O clean	O continent
X claim	O connect	X county
X cruel	O called	X chariot

1. The winner is ______________.

O restless	O radish	O raisin
O runway	X rotten	O relate
X reacted	X require	X rushed

2. The winner is ______________.

O afloat	O agree	X appreciate
X awkward	O assure	X auditorium
O ankle	O apply	X alphabet

3. The winner is ______________.

O system	O slither	X select
O suggest	X slender	X soar
O surrender	O society	X succeed

4. The winner is ______________.

X freckle	X fact	X forecast
O fade	O freeze	O fled
O full	X fantastic	O fourteen

5. The winner is ______________.

X mineral	X middle	O mosquito
O mild	O multiply	O massive
X murmur	X migrate	X mutter

6. The winner is ______________.

Writing Application: Instructions

Think of something you have made. It might be a painting, a model, or something you cooked. Write five sentences telling how you made it. Use an action verb in each sentence. Underline the action verbs.

Name ______________________________

2 Direct Objects

The students helped the **astronomers**. *(helped whom?)*

Astronomers examine the **stars**. *(examine what?)*

They observe **them** with telescopes. *(observe what?)*

Underline the action verb in each sentence. Write the direct object.

1. Maria Mitchell studied the stars. ____________
2. As a child, she helped her father with his work. ____________
3. Her father encouraged his daughter. ____________
4. At the age of twelve, she observed an eclipse. ____________
5. After that she increased her knowledge. ____________
6. She watched the sky at night through a telescope. ____________
7. She read many books about astronomy. ____________
8. In 1847 Maria Mitchell discovered a comet. ____________
9. She gained fame through this discovery. ____________
10. The King of Denmark honored Mitchell. ____________
11. She won a gold medal. ____________
12. The American Academy of Arts and Sciences elected her as a member. ____________
13. As the first female member, she paved the way for others. ____________
14. Vassar College hired the scientist. ____________
15. She continued her work in astronomy. ____________
16. Mitchell taught it as a subject. ____________
17. She helped her students with research. ____________
18. As a teacher, Mitchell influenced future astronomers. ____________

(continued)

Name ______________________________

2 Direct Objects *(continued from page 38)*

Challenge

This newspaper story tells about an important discovery. What is it? Explain by completing each sentence below with a direct object.

News Service National 20:30:08 ************** 01-25-00

Dr. Carmelita Sanchez discovered a ____________ today. She was working in her laboratory when she suddenly noticed a ____________. She grabbed her ____________ and checked the ____________.

Dr. Sanchez tested the ____________. First, she dropped ____________ into water. Then she inspected the ____________ ____________. Nothing had changed. She tried a ____________ ____________. It didn't work. Finally, she tried ____________. It changed the ____________. She had completed her ____________.

Her assistants helped ____________. They repeated the ____________. They proved the ____________.

Officials praise ____________. They say that the discovery aids ____________. Dr. Sanchez received a ____________ for her accomplishment.

****

Writing Application: A Post Card

You have just landed on the moon. Write a post card to a friend, telling what you have found there. Use at least three action verbs and three direct objects. Circle the direct objects.

Name ______________________

3 Main Verbs and Helping Verbs

helping verb main verb

My parents **have left** for the bookstore.

helping verb main verb

They **are going** to the annual book sale.

Write the verb or the verb phrase in each sentence. For each verb phrase, underline the helping verb once and the main verb twice.

1. Our local bookstore is celebrating Mark Twain's birthday.

____

2. The store has lowered the prices of all its books.

____

3. Already, sales have broken all records.

____

4. Yesterday my parents planned their purchases.

____

5. They are buying many books for gifts.

____

6. I am looking for a book by Mark Twain.

____

7. However, Mark Twain's books were selling quickly all morning.

____

8. Many copies of my favorite books had disappeared by noon.

____

9. The clerks were piling other books on the tables.

____

10. I will get there earlier next year.

____

(continued)

Name ____________________

3 Main Verbs and Helping Verbs *(continued from page 40)*

Challenge

The first sentence of a story is very important. Read these first sentences. Underline the main verb and the helping verb in each sentence.

"Nothing had gone right that day."

"The mysterious woman and her package had disappeared."

"As usual the twins were arguing with each other."

Now write your own first sentence for each of the stories below. Use a main verb and a helping verb in each sentence.

1. **A story about a gas station:** ____________________

2. **A story about space travel:** ____________________

3. **A story about your school:** ____________________

4. **A story about your relatives:** ____________________

5. **A story about the future:** ____________________

6. **A story about a sports star:** ____________________

7. **A story about rock music:** ____________________

Writing Application: A Report

Write five sentences, telling about a visit that you made to a library or a bookstore. Use a main verb and a helping verb in each sentence.

Name ______________________________

4 Linking Verbs

Linking verbs	Hawaii's nickname **is** the Aloha State. Hawaii **looks** beautiful.
Action verbs	The tourist **looks** at the map of Hawaii. The map **shows** many tourist attractions.

A Write the verb in each sentence. Label each verb *linking* or *action*.

1. Hawaii is the youngest state in the United States.

____

2. Hawaii's attractions are famous.

____

3. To a visitor, these islands look spectacular.

____

4. The mild climate feels perfect.

____

5. Visitors feel the warm sun and the cool ocean breezes.

____

6. They enjoy the warm waters of the Pacific Ocean.

____

B Underline the linking verb in each sentence. Draw an arrow showing the words that the verb links.

7. Farm products are a source of income for Hawaiians.
8. Foreign markets seem interested in the islands' many crops.
9. Sugar cane is Hawaii's most important product.
10. Pineapples are its second largest crop.
11. Other fruits appear plentiful on the islands as well.
12. The air smells sweet with the scent of coconuts and bananas.

(continued)

Grade 5: Unit 3 Verbs *(Use with pupil book pages 102–103.)*
Skill: Students will identify action verbs, linking verbs, predicate nouns, and predicate adjectives.

Name ____________________

4 Linking Verbs (continued from page 42)

Challenge

You are visiting the imaginary tropical island of Tralala. Complete the following sentences about the island. Write a linking verb in each box. Then add words that name or describe the subject of the sentence.

1. The climate of this island [ ] ____________________
2. The flowers here [ ] ____________________
3. The animals on the island [ ] ____________________
4. Strange fruits [ ] ____________________
5. Several bubbling streams [ ] ____________________
6. The people on this island [ ] ____________________
7. A huge bird [ ] ____________________

Writing Application: A Report

Write five sentences describing your state, province, or city. Use a linking verb from the box below in each sentence.

am	is	are	was	were	will be
look	feel	taste	smell	seem	appear

Name ______________________________

5 Present Tense

George **enjoys** cooking.	We **enjoy** cooking.
He **guesses** the ingredients.	You **guess** the ingredients.
The chef **coaches** George.	Both chefs **coach** George.
Cool air **refreshes** him.	These two fans **refresh** him.
Cooking **relaxes** George.	George and the chef **relax**.
He **tries** new recipes.	I **try** new recipes.

A Write the correct present tense form of each verb in parentheses.

1. My brother Pete ______________ wonderful meals. **(fix)**
2. He ______________ time and care. **(take)**
3. He ______________ the lettuce. **(wash)**
4. Then he ______________ it carefully. **(dry)**
5. The timer ______________. **(buzz)**
6. My sisters ______________ into the kitchen. **(rush)**
7. We all ______________ the dinner. **(enjoy)**

B 8–15. This list of chores has eight incorrect verbs. Use proofreading marks to write their correct present tense.

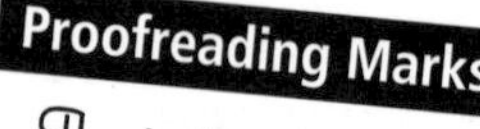

Proofreading Marks
- ¶ Indent
- ∧ Add
- Delete
- ≡ Capital letter
- / Small letter

Example: Mom cooks ~~cook~~ a lot of dinners for us.

Proofreading

To-Do List

- Mom and Dad cooks the vegetables, and Mom frys the meat.
- Lena peeles the potatoes and makes the salad.
- Dad mashs the potatoes and mix's the salad dressing.
- Jenna set the table and clears the dishes.
- Lawrence and Jenna washes and drys the dishes.

(continued)

Grade 5: Unit 3 Verbs *(Use with pupil book pages 104–105.)*
Skill: Students will use present tense verbs correctly with singular and plural subjects.

Name ______________________________

5 Present Tense (continued from page 44)

Challenge

Classroom Cookery, a television show, is captioned for people who have difficulty hearing. Below are scenes from four different episodes. Explain what is happening in each scene by completing the caption below each picture. Use a verb in the present tense form in each sentence.

1.

Cecil and Ron ______________________

____

2.

He ______________________________

____

3.

Ming Chen ______________________

____

4.

The girls ______________________

____

Writing Application: A Progress Report

The Parents' Association has hired the students in your class to prepare a special luncheon. Students are busy preparing the food, setting up the room, and putting up decorations. You are in charge of the event. Write a progress report for the Parents' Association. Use the present tense form of five verbs from the box below.

arrange	push	carry	toss	fix	scrub	reach	make

Name ______________________________

6 Past Tense

Eric **watched** the workers.
He **saved** his questions for later.
The workers **stayed** for a long time.
Then they **hurried** to the next job.
They **scrubbed** the kettles thoroughly.

A Complete each sentence by writing the past tense form of the verb in parentheses.

1. Eric ____________ about colonists' crafts while visiting Williamsburg. **(learn)**
2. The colonists ____________ their own soap. **(produce)**
3. They ____________ ashes from their fireplaces. **(use)**
4. They ____________ water through the ashes in a barrel. **(pour)**
5. The brown water ____________ out through a hole near the bottom. **(drip)**
6. People ____________ this liquid lye. **(call)**
7. The women ____________ the lye in a kettle. **(cook)**
8. They added fats and grease ____________ from their cooking. **(supply)**
9. The mixture ____________ into a jelly that they used for soap. **(turn)**

B **10–16.** Use proofreading marks to correct seven past tense verbs in this colonial journal entry.

Example: Long ago we ^used ~~use~~ lye to make soap.

Proofreading Marks

¶ Indent
^ Add
Delete
≡ Capital letter
/ Small letter

Proofreading

Thursday, September 2

Today we made soap. For days in advance we pland and prepared. We carryd firewood and water, and we wash and dryed the kettles.

This morning, Mother boilled the liquid, and we stired it. When the soap was ready, Mother placd it into big pans. It was still soft when it cooled.

(continued)

Grade 5: Unit 3 Verbs *(Use with pupil book pages 106–107.)*
Skill: Students will form the past tense of regular verbs.

Name ______________________________

6 Past Tense (continued from page 46)

Challenge

The year is 2588. You have just returned from a time-machine trip back to 2001. While you were on your trip, you took pictures of the machines that people used in 2001. Explain how the people used these machines. Write a sentence for each picture. Use a different past tense verb in each sentence.

Writing Application: A Story Idea

A time machine has taken you back to the time of the North American colonists. Now you have returned to the present. Write a paragraph, telling your friends about what you saw. Use at least five past tense verbs. Circle the verbs.

Name ____________________

7 Future Tense

We **shall stay** here this summer.
My brother **will work** next July.

Underline the verb or verb phrase in each sentence. Then rewrite each sentence, using the future tense form of the underlined verb.

1. This summer Eva has traveled to New Mexico.

   ____

2. Each year she visits her Aunt Nina, who is a scientist.

   ____

3. Eva helps with the research.

   ____

4. They work at a large pueblo ruin.

   ____

5. They have traced the development of the pueblo.

   ____

6. The scientists have used the latest research techniques.

   ____

7. Their findings have provided information about the Mimbres people.

   ____

8. Aunt Nina and Eva dig with care.

   ____

9. They search for Mimbres pottery.

   ____

10. Eva has learned much about archaeology.

    ____

(continued)

Name ______________________________

7 Future Tense *(continued from page 48)*

Challenge

The symbols below are taken from an ancient Egyptian form of writing called hieroglyphics. Scientists often find this kind of writing in Egyptian ruins. Use the meanings of the symbols to write a sentence for each group of symbols below. Use a future tense verb in each sentence.

person	**see**	**woods, tree**	**write**
cut, knife	**plants**	**buildings**	**animals**
foreign country	**water**	**go, walk**	**books, paintings**
eat, speak	**food**	**boat, sail**	**steps, climb**

1. ______________________________
2. ______________________________
3. ______________________________
4. ______________________________
5. ______________________________
6. ______________________________

Now draw two hieroglyphic sentences of your own. Then write each sentence, using a future tense verb.

7. ______________________________
8. ______________________________

Writing Application: A Vacation Plan

Write a paragraph, describing your plans for next summer. Your plans can be real or imaginary. Use a future tense verb in each sentence. Underline each verb.

Name ______________________________

Writing with Verbs

Sentences with the same subject	Mick went to the zoo. Mick saw lots of different animals. Mick watched the dolphin show.
Combined sentence	Mick went to the zoo**,** saw lots of different animals**, and** watched the dolphin show.

Combining Sentences 1–4. Combine the predicates in each set of sentences in these picture captions. When combining two predicates, do not use a comma. When combining three predicates, set off each one with a comma.

Revising

Rabbits are more active at night. Rabbits do not scamper far from cover.

Elephants are very affectionate. Elephants stroke each other with their trunks.

Mammals use their sharp senses to identify enemies. They use their sharp senses to hunt for food. Mammals use their sharp senses to find shelter.

A cat's whiskers keep it from bumping into things. The whiskers let the cat know whether it has enough room.

1. ______________________________

____

2. ______________________________

____

3. ______________________________

____

4. ______________________________

____

Grade 5: Unit 3 Verbs *(Use with pupil book pages 110–111.)*
Skill: Students will combine sentences, using the conjunctions *and* or *or* to create compound predicates.

Name ______________________________

Writing with Verbs *(continued from page 50)*

Different verb tense	Mammals had four kinds of teeth. Incisor teeth cut. Canine teeth tore. Premolars and molars grind.
Same verb tense	Mammals **have** four kinds of teeth. Incisor teeth **cut**. Canine teeth **tear**. Premolars and molars **grind**.

Keeping Verbs in the Same Tense 5–14. Rewrite this part of a class trip report to show that the action took place yesterday. Check each underlined verb for correct tense.

Revising

The Museum of Natural History

Yesterday we go to the Museum of Natural History. The guide shows us teeth from different animals. It was like the teeth models at the orthodontist's office, but much more interesting. The beaver's incisors were orange! The guide will show us a bear's strong molars. This bear eats berries, fruits, small animals, and of course, honey. Then the guide takes out chimpanzee teeth. They look almost like mine! She points to the chimpanzee's large canine teeth. Those will be different from everything in the orthodontist's office.

Name ______________________________

8 Subject-Verb Agreement

Singular Subjects	Plural Subjects	*I* or *you*
Cleo **rides** the bus.	The girls **ride** the bus.	You **ride** the bus.
She **enjoys** the ride.	We **enjoy** the ride.	I **enjoy** the ride.
My brother **catches** the bus.	Cleo and I **catch** the bus.	You **catch** the bus.

Rewrite each sentence, using the correct present tense form of the verb in parentheses.

1. My brother __?__ for the government. **(work)**

____

2. He __?__ public transportation. **(plan)**

____

3. Public transportation __?__ trains, subways, and buses. **(include)**

____

4. It __?__ people and the environment. **(help)**

____

5. My brother and I __?__ problems in public transportation. **(discuss)**

____

6. We __?__ about the increase in automobile traffic. **(talk)**

____

7. The roads __?__ more crowded each year. **(become)**

____

8. My brother and other workers __?__ different solutions. **(try)**

____

9. They __?__ the use of public transportation. **(encourage)**

____

10. Now I __?__ the bus whenever possible. **(ride)**

____

(continued)

Name ______________________________

8 Subject-Verb Agreement *(continued from page 52)*

Challenge

Read the bus schedule below and answer the questions that follow. Each answer should be a complete sentence that uses a verb in the present tense form. Try to use a different subject for each sentence.

	ARRIVES				
	COBURN	**TYVILLE**	**MAXTON**	**SIMPSON**	**JEROME**
LEAVES	9:30 A.M.	10:00 A.M.	10:10 A.M.	10:15 A.M.	10:20 A.M.
	11:00 A.M.	11:30 A.M.	11:40 A.M.	11:45 A.M.	11:50 A.M.
	1:30 P.M.	2:00 P.M.	2:10 P.M.	2:15 P.M.	2:20 P.M.

1. When does the first bus leave Coburn in the morning?

____

2. When does the 1:30 P.M. bus arrive in Tyville?

____

3. What time do I get to Maxton if I take the 11:00 A.M. bus?

____

4. Which two stops come between Tyville and Jerome?

____

5. What do people call the last stop on the line?

____

6. How do I get to Simpson before 10:30 A.M.?

____

Writing Application: A Travel Diary

You and a friend are taking a trip by bus, car, or train. Write at least five sentences for your diary, telling about what happens on the journey. Use the present tense form of a verb in each sentence. Make sure each verb agrees with its subject.

Name ____________________

9 Agreement with *be* and *have*

Subjects	Forms of *be*	Forms of *have*
I	am, was	have, had
he, she, it	is, was	has, had
singular nouns	is, was	has, had
you, we, they	are, were	have, had
plural nouns	are, were	have, had

A The underlined verb in each sentence does not agree with its subject. Rewrite each sentence correctly.

1. Has you ever built a model airplane?

____

2. I is building one now.

____

3. It are a free-flight model with no wires.

____

4. This model have a wingspan of six feet.

____

B **5–12.** This living history presentation has eight errors in subject-verb agreement. Use proofreading marks to correct the verbs.

Example: Last night I ~~were~~ ^was building a model of a plane.

Proofreading

I is Wilbur Wright, and this are my brother, Orville. We am the builders of the first airplane. We had a bicycle shop that were very successful. When I were sick, I had time to read about flying. Later, we built a flying machine. We was ready to fly. Orville have his chance first, and he flew twelve seconds. Later, I was able to fly the machine for almost a full minute. Do you has any questions?

(continued)

Grade 5: Unit 3 Verbs *(Use with pupil book pages 114–115.)*
Skill: Students will write forms of *be* and *have* to agree with singular and plural subjects.

Name ______________________________

9 Agreement with *be* and *have* (continued from page 54)

Challenge

Captain Chang's plane has encountered rough weather. She has radioed for help, but static has made parts of the air traffic controller's answer impossible to understand. Help Captain Chang by rewriting the answer. Use a form of *be* or *have* wherever you run into static!

Roger, Flight 555. We /\/\/\ you on radar. We /\/\/\ reading you, and your request /\/\/\ been received. The weather you /\/\/\ experiencing /\/\/\ a low-pressure area stretching from Springdale to Winter Valley. The storm /\/\/\ moving at twenty-five miles per hour due east. You /\/\/\ passed the center of the storm and /\/\/\ out of danger. We /\/\/\ routing you through Summerville, however, because another storm front /\/\/\ approached from the north. At present your altitude /\/\/\ holding steady. It looks as if the worst /\/\/\ over. We /\/\/\ transferred you to air traffic control at Summerville. Good luck. Over.

____

____

____

____

____

____

____

____

____

____

Writing Application: A Story

You are so small that you can fit into a model plane. Write a paragraph about a trip you take. Use forms of *be* and *have* in your sentences. Make sure that the verbs agree with their subjects.

Name ______________________________

10 Contractions with *not*

Verb + *not*	Contraction	Verb + *not*	Contraction
do not	don't	has not	hasn't
did not	didn't	had not	hadn't
is not	isn't	would not	wouldn't
were not	weren't	cannot	can't
will not	won't	must not	mustn't

A Write the contraction for each underlined word or words.

1. Max, I cannot go to the concert with you. ____________
2. Are you not feeling well? ____________
3. I do not have my science report finished yet. ____________
4. Dad will not let me go until it is done. ____________
5. I had not done my research until this week. ____________
6. I did not know it would take this much time. ____________

B **7–12.** Use proofreading marks to correct six contractions in this e-mail message.

Example: Arthur ~~wasnt~~ **wasn't** finished with his science report.

Proofreading Marks
- ¶ Indent
- ∧ Add
- Delete
- ≡ Capital letter
- / Small letter

Proofreading — e-mail

Subject: Sorry!
Date: November 22, 2001 05:20:19 pm
Sender: Arthur Lopez
To: Max McGee

Hi! I am sorry I can't go to the concert. I'm glad I was'nt the only one going to the concert with you. I wouldnt want to spoil your fun. Josh cann't wait to hear the concert. There were'nt enough tickets for all of us last time. Remember? Also, I havent forgotten how great the last concert was. I have learned I should'nt wait until the last minute to write my report.

(continued)

Name ______________________________

10 Contractions with *not* (continued from page 56)

Challenge

You are writing a science report on safety. Write two sentences that tell about each picture set. In the first sentence, tell what to do. In the second sentence, tell what not to do. Use a different contraction in the second sentence of each pair.

1. 

____
____
____

2. 

____
____
____

3. 

____
____
____

4. 

____
____
____

Writing Application: A Letter

You were supposed to go somewhere with a friend, and now you find that you are unable to go. Write a letter of apology, explaining what has happened. Include at least five contractions that use the word *not.*

Name ______________________________

11 Regular and Irregular Verbs

	Verb	Past Tense	Past with Helping Verb
Regular verbs	paint	painted	(has, have, had) painted
	hire	hired	(has, have, had) hired
	spy	spied	(has, have, had) spied
Irregular verbs	go	went	(has, have, had) gone
	think	thought	(has, have, had) thought

A In the first column, write the past tense form of each underlined verb. In the second, write the past form of the verb when it is used with a helping verb.

1. We start a class newspaper. __________ have __________
2. We go to the newspaper office. __________ had __________
3. We come back with good ideas. __________ had __________
4. We try them out. __________ have __________
5. Eduardo brings his camera. __________ has __________
6. He takes good pictures. __________ has __________

B **7–12.** This news story has six incorrect verb forms. Use proofreading marks to correct the news story.

Example: She had ~~hope~~ **hoped** to write many news stories.

Proofreading Marks

- ¶ Indent
- ∧ Add
- Delete
- ≡ Capital letter
- / Small letter

Proofreading

Adams Middle School

Victory for the Track Team

Adams Middle School taked first place at the track meet last Saturday. Marissa Stein runned her best time by two seconds. Gail Briski had overcomed a sore ankle and jump to victory. The 440-yard relay pressed hard all the way to the finish line. "When I saw how the girls hand the baton to one another, I knew we was going to win," said the coach.

(continued)

Name ______________________________

11 Regular and Irregular Verbs (continued from page 58)

Challenge

Nina Newsworthy is interviewing two candidates for class president. Help Nina finish her interview. Complete each candidate's answers. Use a past form of a verb from the box in each of your answers.

run	bring	come	go	make	say	take	think	write

Nina: What schools have you attended in the past?

Candidate 1: I have ______________________________.

Candidate 2: I ______________________________.

Nina: Have you ever run for a class office before?

Candidate 1: I ______________________________.

Candidate 2: I ______________________________.

Nina: What class projects have you been involved in?

Candidate 1: I ______________________________.

Candidate 2: I have ______________________________.

Nina: What do you think the class has accomplished in the past year?

Candidate 1: The class ______________________________.

Candidate 2: We ______________________________.

Nina: What should be the class's major concern for next year?

Candidate 1: I ______________________________.

Candidate 2: I have ______________________________.

Writing Application: A Job Application

You are applying for a job as either a newspaper photographer or reporter. Write five sentences about pictures that you have taken or articles that you have written. Use past forms of five of the verbs from the box below.

bring	come	go	make	say	take	think	write

Name ______________________________

12 More Irregular Verbs

Verb	Past Tense	Past with Helping Verb
sing	sang	(has, have, had) sung
begin	began	(has, have, had) begun
wear	wore	(has, have, had) worn
choose	chose	(has, have, had) chosen
grow	grew	(has, have, had) grown

A Rewrite each sentence. Use the correct past form of the verb in parentheses.

1. Ivan _?_ a glance at the thermometer. **(steal)**

____

2. He had _?_ winter was coming. **(know)**

____

3. It _?_ with the first cold spell. **(begin)**

____

4. That morning in October, he had _?_ in the pond. **(swim)**

____

5. In the afternoon, it had _?_ cold. **(grow)**

____

B **6–10.** Use proofreading marks to correct five errors in this report.

Example: She had ~~chose~~ **chosen** to wear her warmest coat.

Proofreading Marks

- ¶ Indent
- ∧ Add
- Delete
- ≡ Capital letter
- / Small letter

Weather Watch

The warm spell has broke. Last night an ice storm ringed in the evening, bringing winds that blowed all night. By morning, winds had tore branches off trees and ice had frozen some telephone lines. Winter has began.

(continued)

Grade 5: Unit 3 Verbs *(Use with pupil book pages 120–121.)*
Skill: Students will write the past and past participle forms of irregular verbs.

Name ______________________________

12 More Irregular Verbs *(continued from page 60)*

Challenge

Write six alphabet sentences. Use a past form of a verb from the box below. Then write a sentence, using words that begin with the same letter as the verb. Each sentence must have at least four words. The first sentence has been done for you.

ring	begin	break	freeze	fly
swim	wear	choose	grow	tear

1. **Five flocks of feathered finch had flown from the forest.**
2. ______________________________
3. ______________________________
4. ______________________________
5. ______________________________
6. ______________________________

Writing Application: A List

Write five sentences about how you once knew that spring was coming. In each sentence, use a past form of one of the verbs from the box below.

sing	begin	blow	know
swim	wear	grow	fly

Name ____________________

13 Verb Phrases with *have*

Verb Phrases	Verb Phrases with Contractions
I **could have tried** to go.	I **could've tried** to go.
You **would have enjoyed** the day.	You **would've enjoyed** the day.
We **should have packed** a picnic.	We **should've packed** a picnic.
She **must have seen** the float.	She **must've seen** the float.

A Rewrite the verb phrase in each sentence so that it includes a contraction.

1. You should have seen that parade! ____________
2. I could have gotten there earlier. ____________
3. It must have been a good one. ____________
4. I could have left my house earlier. ____________
5. I should have remembered the time. ____________
6. You would have liked our float. ____________
7. I could have taken a picture of it for you. ____________
8. People must have come from miles away. ____________
9. The children would have watched the show all day. ____________
10. They must have stayed for at least two hours. ____________

B Write the verb phrase in each sentence so that it does not include a contraction. If the verb phrase is incorrect, write it correctly.

11. You should've seen my mother in the band. ____________
12. Her music would of amazed you. ____________
13. She must've practiced for months. ____________
14. She could of passed for a professional musician. ____________
15. The band should've had more time. ____________
16. They must of been the best act in the parade. ____________

(continued)

Name ______________________________

13 Verb Phrases with *have* (continued from page 62)

Challenge

The members of the Nature Club are having problems making their float. Help them by writing a solution to each problem shown in the pictures below. Try to use a different verb phrase with *have* or *'ve* in each sentence.

____

____

____

____

____

____

____

____

Writing Application: A Journal

You were once a clown in a parade. Write six sentences about your act. Use a different verb phrase with *have* in each sentence.

Name ______________________________

14 teach, learn; let, leave

Will you **teach** me about camps?
I would like to **learn** how to find a good one.
Will your mother **let** you go?
She said I could **leave** for camp next summer.
I must **leave** my dog at home.

A Complete each sentence with the correct word in parentheses.

1. Mr. Berg will ______________ us about camping. **(teach, learn)**
2. Students will ______________ about many kinds of camps. **(teach, learn)**
3. Teachers ______________ the campers work independently. **(let, leave)**
4. Campers ______________ to do things on their own. **(teach, learn)**
5. Their parents ______________ them go to overnight camp. **(let, leave)**
6. At camp they ______________ how to live outdoors. **(teach, learn)**

B **7–12.** This letter has six errors in the use of *teach*, *learn*, *let*, and *leave*. Use proofreading marks to correct the letter.

Example: Mom, please ~~leave~~ **let** me make my own decision about camp.

Proofreading

Proofreading Marks

- ¶ Indent
- ∧ Add
- Delete
- ≡ Capital letter
- / Small letter

Dear Mom,

Please let your doubts behind and leave me go to camp. The counselors will learn us to ride horses. We will learn how to swim. This experience will help me grow and leave me be proud of myself. I will teach so many things by being part of the camp. Please leave me show you that this is a good idea.

Love,

Meg

(continued)

Name ___________________________

14 teach, learn; let, leave (continued from page 64)

Challenge

It is visiting day at camp. Use the map below to answer the visitors' questions. Write a complete sentence for each answer. Use the words *teach, learn, let,* and *leave* in your answers.

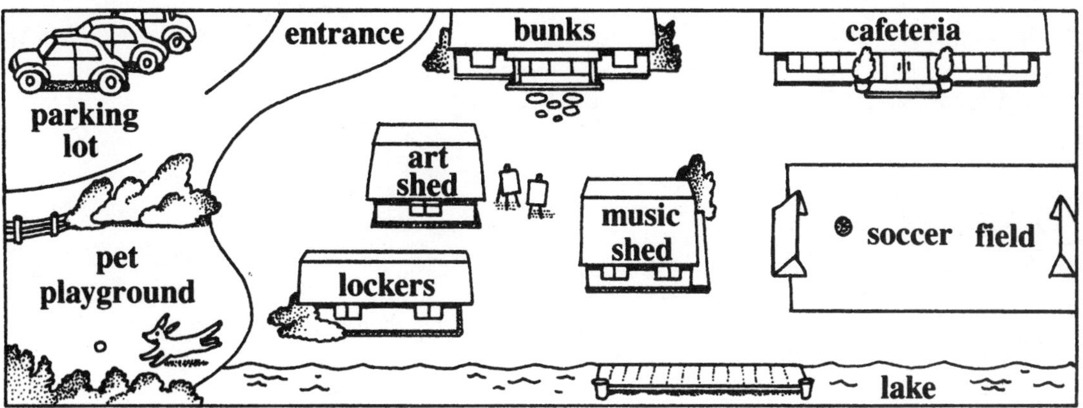

1. Where do I park my car?

____

2. Where can my dog run?

____

3. Where can we sing the new camp song?

____

4. Where can I watch the coach instructing the soccer team?

____

Now write one more question a visitor might ask. Then write your answer, using the verb *teach, learn, let,* or *leave.*

5. ___________________________

____

Writing Application: A Letter

You are at summer camp. Write a letter to your relatives at home. Tell them what you are doing. Use the verbs *teach*, *learn*, *let*, and *leave*.

Name ______________________________

15 sit, set; can, may

I **sit** in a big, comfortable chair.
I **set** my appointment card on the front desk.
I **can** hear the dentist's drill.
May I go home now?

A One verb in each sentence is used incorrectly. Rewrite each sentence correctly.

1. Please set in the waiting room until the dentist is ready.

____

2. You can come in now.

____

3. Set in the large chair by the sink.

____

4. Sit your books on the table by the window.

____

B 5–8. Use proofreading marks to correct four errors in the use of *sit, set, can,* and *may* in this poster.

Example: You need to  ~~set~~ sit quietly while the dentist checks your teeth.

Proofreading

Proofreading Marks
¶ Indent
∧ Add
Delete
≡ Capital letter
/ Small letter

How Parents Help Us Care for Our Teeth

- Parents may help their children learn to care for their teeth.
- They can set nearby and watch as their young children brush.
- They can sit the toothpaste within easy reach.
- They may set a good example by brushing frequently.

(continued)

Name ______________________________

15 *sit, set; can, may* (continued from page 66)

Challenge

The inventors of the machines below thought that their inventions would help people take care of their teeth. The only problem was that no one could figure out how to use them. Write two sentences of instructions for each invention. Use the verb *sit, set, can,* or *may* in each sentence.

1. Max Grogl invented a switch that turns off the dentist's drill when the patient wants to say, "Ouch!"

____

____

____

____

2. Martina Vesper invented the combination toothbrush-radio that makes brushing your teeth more fun.

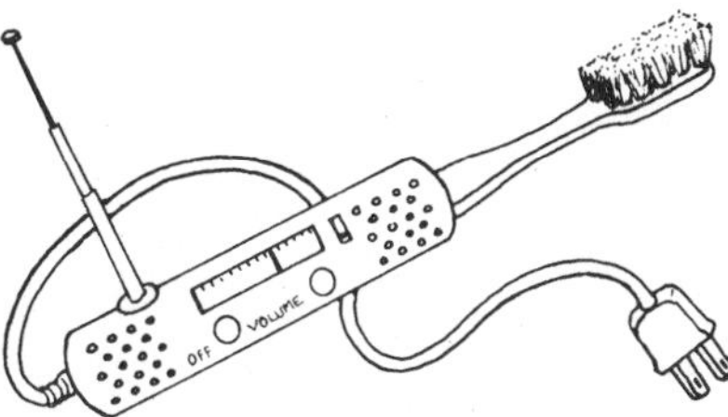

____

____

____

____

Now draw your own dental invention. Write two sentences that tell about it.

____

____

____

____

Writing Application: A Health Manual

Write six instructions a dentist might give you for taking care of your teeth. Include the verbs *sit, set, can,* and *may* in your instructions.

Name ______________________________

Using Exact Verbs

> adore
> I like that magnificent photo by Ansel Adams.

1–10. Revise this advertisement from an electronic bulletin board. Replace each underlined verb with a more exact verb from each pair of words in the word box. Be sure the exact verb you choose fits the meaning of the sentence. Cross out the weak verb and write the exact verb above it.

purchasing	trading	serve	stimulate
grab	snap	mimic	act
handle	employ	beg	question
amuse	delight	win	earn
taking	owning	slap	locate

Revising

e-mail

Is anyone interested in getting a box camera? You can take terrific photos with this old camera, and it's not that hard to use. Trust me—the results will please you. You'll find that having a fine camera will help your creativity. On photo shoots, you'll be a pro. Strangers will ask you to photograph them. By the way, good photographers get big bucks. How would you like to put a hundred-dollar price tag on one of your pictures?

Name ______________________________

1 What Is an Adjective?

What kind	**Nervous, impatient** travelers stood at the rail. They were **weary** and **hungry**.
How many	**Many** immigrants had come before them.

Write each adjective and the noun or the pronoun that it describes. Do not include *a, an,* or *the.*

1. A single ship moved toward the bustling harbor.

____

2. It was noisy and crowded.

____

3. Many adults were happy and talkative.

____

4. They were eager to reach the final destination.

____

5. Two small girls peered toward the distant land.

____

6. They were curious about the future.

____

7. Would they like living in the large, strange country?

____

8. Suddenly they heard several joyous shouts.

____

9. An enormous, majestic statue appeared on the horizon.

____

10. The brilliant torch welcomed the travelers to a new home.

____

(continued)

Name ______________________________

1 What Is an Adjective? *(continued from page 69)*

Challenge

Printed below are the words *The Statue of Liberty.* On the line next to each letter, write a group of words consisting of one noun or pronoun and at least two adjectives. Every word should begin with the letter at the beginning of the line. The first one has been done for you.

T twelve timid travelers

H ______________________________

E ______________________________

S ______________________________

T ______________________________

A ______________________________

T ______________________________

U ______________________________

E ______________________________

O ______________________________

F ______________________________

L ______________________________

I ______________________________

B ______________________________

E ______________________________

R ______________________________

T ______________________________

Y ______________________________

Writing Application: A Description

You and your family are moving to a new country. What will your new home be like? Write at least five sentences describing your new home. Use two adjectives in each sentence.

Name ____________________

Writing with Adjectives

Sentence	Tigers live on the slopes of the Himalayas.
Elaborated sentence	Rare orange and black striped Bengal tigers live on the southern slopes of the Himalayas.

Elaborating Sentences 1–4. These picture captions are from a book about elephants. Elaborate the sentences with adjectives.

Revising

1. The biggest land animal is the elephant.

2. A herd of elephants came to the waterhole.

3. An elephant calf rolled in the mud.

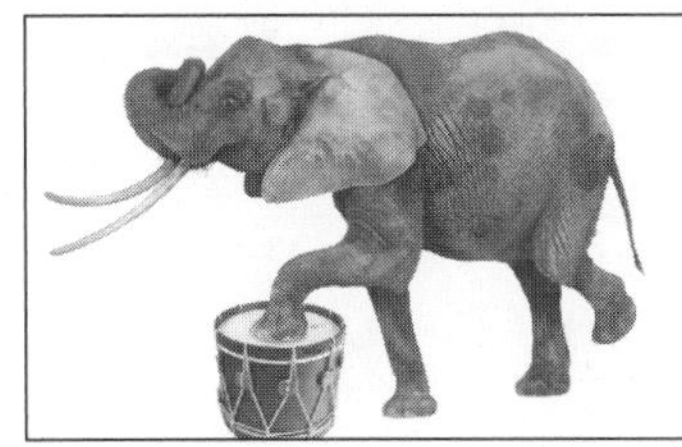

4. An elephant performs in a circus.

1. ____

____

2. ____

____

3. ____

____

4. ____

____

(continued)

Name ____________________

Writing with Adjectives *(continued from page 71)*

Two sentences	The moon reflects the light of the sun. The moon shines.
Combined sentence	The **shining** moon reflects the light of the sun.

Combining Sentences 5–8. Use adjectives to combine each set of underlined sentences in these paragraphs from a report about the moon. Add *-y, -ed, or -ing* to form adjectives, as needed.

Revising

The moon is our nearest neighbor in space. There are craters on the moon's surface. The craters are huge. The moon's surface looks hard and gray. Lunar soil is covered with a layer of dust. The dust sparkles. The moon has no air, water, plants, or animals. The moon is lifeless.

If the moon is a ball of cold, hard rock, how does it shine? The moon is like a giant mirror. It reflects light from the sun. Only a tiny bit of sunlight makes the moon shine. The sunlight is bright.

Grammar

Name ___________________________________

2 Articles and Demonstratives

Articles	**A** storm is predicted. Do you have **an** umbrella or **an** old raincoat? **The** rain should begin soon.
Demonstrative adjectives	**This** forecast is more accurate than **that** one. **These** reports are better than **those** reports.

Rewrite each sentence, using the correct word in parentheses.

1. (A, An) long time ago, there were no daily weather reports.

   ____

2. In (these, those) days, people couldn't predict weather as we can today.

   ____

3. That age was not as scientific as (this, that) one.

   ____

4. At (that, this) time, people depended more on natural signs.

   ____

5. Roosting birds were (a, an) indication of rain.

   ____

6. A red sky at night meant that (an, the) next day would be fair.

   ____

7. Red lightning meant that (a, an) storm was approaching.

   ____

8. In (those, these) days, weather prediction was less exact than now.

   ____

9. However, forecasters still use (these, those) signs of long ago.

   ____

10. (A, An) accurate forecast is the product of many different methods.

    ____

(continued)

Name ____________________

2 Articles and Demonstratives *(continued from page 73)*

Challenge

Discover tomorrow's weather forecast. Color the spaces containing nouns that can be used with the article or the demonstrative adjective at the beginning of each row.

the	day	map		seas	snow	rain		wind	sky	ice
an	inn	sky	wind	eagle	day	age	map	ear	sea	clouds
a	city	icicle	eel	winter	ace	frost	egg	storm	ocean	uncle
this	time	night	cities	front	seas	spring	clouds	street	rivers	smog
these	clouds	wind	sea	hills	city	days	age	maps	log	charts
that	ocean	hills	clouds	wind	storms	snow	charts	heat	days	fall
those	days	moon	wind	clouds	tides	bees	sun	storms	charts	maps

Now write five sentences about the weather. Create a scene with extreme weather conditions. It can be extremely harsh or very beautiful. In each sentence, use a different article or demonstrative adjective and one of the nouns that you colored.

1. ____________________

2. ____________________

3. ____________________

4. ____________________

5. ____________________

Writing Application: A Weather Report

Write five sentences about natural changes that you might notice before a storm. Use articles and demonstrative adjectives in your sentences.

Grade 5: Unit 4 Adjectives *(Use with pupil book pages 156–157.)*
Skill: Students will use articles and demonstrative adjectives in sentences and in phrases.

Name ____________________

3 Comparing with Adjectives

Adjective	Comparing Two	Comparing Three or More
great	great**er**	great**est**
nice	nic**er**	nic**est**
easy	eas**ier**	eas**iest**
big	bi**gger**	bi**ggest**
important	**more** important	**most** important

A Write the correct form of the adjective in parentheses to complete each sentence.

1. Mozart's story is one of the ______________ in music. **(strange)**
2. He was one of the ______________ composers in the world. **(young)**
3. He was ______________ in music than in other subjects. **(interested)**
4. Few composers had ______________ training than Mozart. **(thorough)**
5. His operas are ______________ than many other operas. **(funny)**
6. Mozart's last days were the ______________ days of all. **(sad)**

B **7–12.** Use proofreading marks to correct six incorrect adjective forms in this television review.

Example: Mozart's popularity is the ~~greater~~ **greatest** it's ever been.

Proofreading Marks

- ¶ Indent
- ∧ Add
- Delete
- ≡ Capital letter
- / Small letter

Proofreading

Mozart: The Man and His Music

Last night I watched one of the finer television shows ever. The show featured the life and music of Mozart, one of the great and brilliant composers of all time. Mozart made a bigger musical contribution than most composers, but his life was one of the sadder and shorter of all. Fortunately, much of his music is lighter and cheerful than his life.

(continued)

Name ____________________

3 Comparing with Adjectives (continued from page 75)

Challenge

Write an adjective beneath the first box in each row. Beneath the second box, write the form of the adjective that compares two. Beneath the third box, write the form of the adjective that compares three or more. Draw pictures to illustrate the three forms of the adjective. An example has been done for you.

ADJECTIVE	COMPARING TWO	COMPARING THREE OR MORE

1. difficult	more difficult	most difficult
	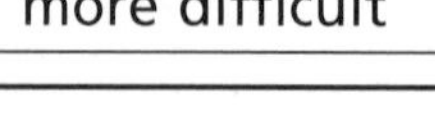 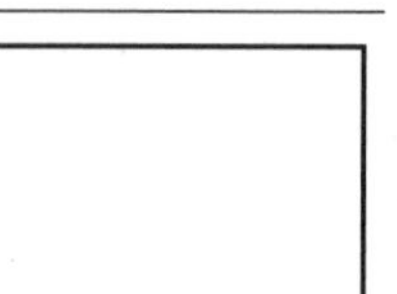	
2. ________	________	________
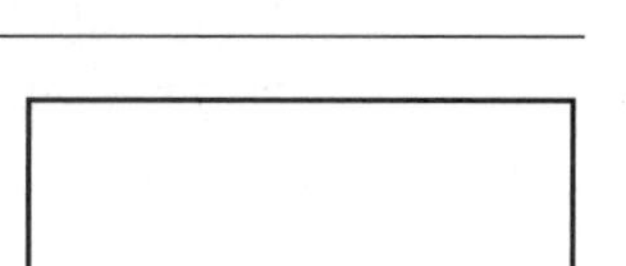	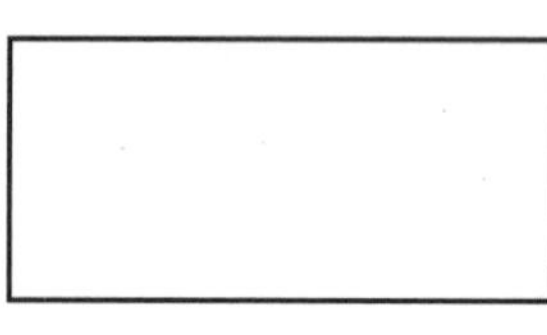	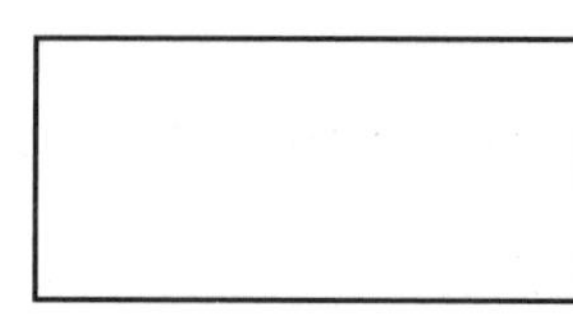
3. ________	________	________
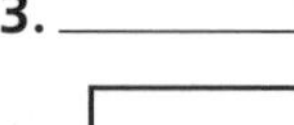 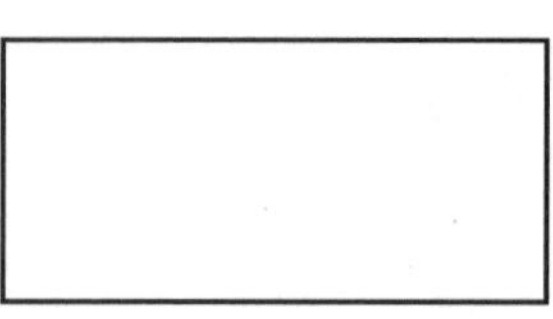	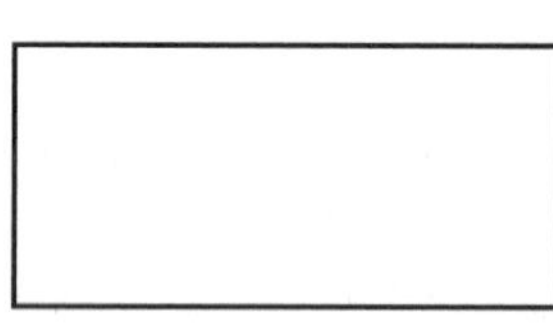	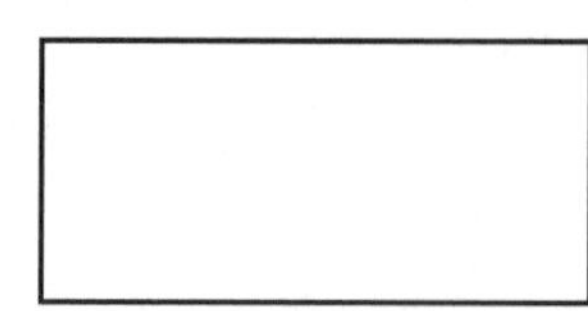
4. ________	________	________

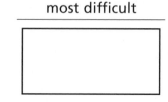

Writing Application: A Music Review

COMPARING AND CONTRASTING

Write six sentences, comparing three songs that you know. Use an adjective that compares in each sentence.

Grade 5: Unit 4 Adjectives *(Use with pupil book pages 158–159.)*
Skill: Students will write the comparative and the superlative forms of adjectives.

Name ___________________________

4 Comparing with *good* and *bad*

Good	Bad
This is a **good** apple.	This looks like a **bad** pear.
This apple is **better** than that one.	It looks **worse** than that pear.
This is the **best** apple I've ever eaten.	It looks like the **worst** pear in the bunch.

A Complete each sentence by writing the correct form of *good* or *bad*.

1. This is the __________ meal I have ever eaten. **(good)**
2. Yes, Benita is a very __________ cook. **(good)**
3. She makes __________ stews than those the restaurant serves. **(good)**
4. The __________ meal I ever had here was a cheese sandwich. **(bad)**
5. The sandwich was __________ than the cafeteria's sandwiches. **(bad)**

B **6–10.** Use proofreading marks to correct five incorrect uses of *good* and *bad* in this thank-you letter.

Example: This sandwich was the ~~best~~ **better** of the two.

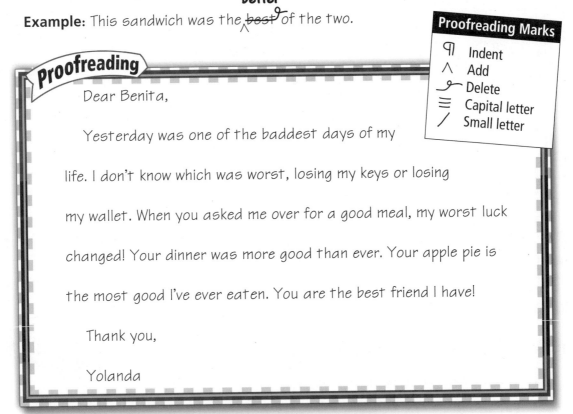

Proofreading Marks

- ¶ Indent
- ∧ Add
- Delete
- ≡ Capital letter
- / Small letter

Proofreading

Dear Benita,

Yesterday was one of the baddest days of my life. I don't know which was worst, losing my keys or losing my wallet. When you asked me over for a good meal, my worst luck changed! Your dinner was more good than ever. Your apple pie is the most good I've ever eaten. You are the best friend I have!

Thank you,

Yolanda

(continued)

Name ______________________________

4 Comparing with *good* and *bad* (continued from page 77)

Challenge

Henrietta reviews restaurants for a newspaper. You can help Henrietta write her next review. Think of a restaurant you know. Fill in the blanks labeled *adjective* with forms of *good* or *bad*. Follow the directions for filling in the other blanks.

______________ (name of restaurant) is a ______________ (adjective) restaurant. In fact, it is probably the ______________ (adjective) ______________ (type of restaurant) restaurant outside ______________ (name of country). The ______________ (name of first dish) is ______________ (adjective) than that served in ______________ (name of city). The ______________ (name of second dish) are the ______________ (adjective) I have ever eaten. Even the ______________ (name of third dish) is ______________ (adjective).

______________ (name of chef), with whom I am acquainted, is a ______________ (adjective) chef. Recently, he was named the ______________ (adjective) chef in the country by ______________ (name of magazine) It's amazing, but every year he gets ______________ (adjective) and ______________ (adjective).

Writing Application: A Report

COMPARING AND CONTRASTING

You have a job inspecting school cafeterias. Write a paragraph, comparing three meals that you have eaten in your school cafeteria. Use the adjectives *good*, *better*, *best*, *bad*, *worse*, and *worst* in your paragraph.

Name ______________________________

5 Proper Adjectives

Proper Nouns	Proper Adjectives
Mexico	**Mexican** food
Greece	**Greek** olives
Africa	**African** fabrics

A Rewrite each sentence, using a proper adjective that is made from the proper noun in parentheses.

1. __?__ cameras were on display at the world trade fair. **(Japan)**

____

2. There was an exhibit of __?__ sculpture. **(North Africa)**

____

3. The __?__ sweaters looked warm. **(Scotland)**

____

B **4–8.** Use proofreading marks to correct five incorrect proper adjectives on this post card.

Example: We bought some west indian baskets.

Proofreading

Dear Juanita,

The world trade fair is like a shopping tour of international markets. I visited the booths of five european countries. I ate hungarian goulash and belgian chocolates. Then I bought a Polish leather jacket and a swiss watch. Finally, I admired the new german cars in candy colors.

Bernardo

Proofreading Marks

- ¶ Indent
- ∧ Add
- Delete
- ≡ Capital letter
- / Small letter

(continued)

Name ______________________________

5 Proper Adjectives (continued from page 79)

Challenge

Use the map to complete the sentences below. Write a proper adjective in each blank. You may use your dictionary.

1. Athens is the ______________________________ capital.
2. Vienna is the ______________________________ capital.
3. Madrid is the ______________________________ capital.
4. Warsaw is the ______________________________ capital.
5. Lisbon is the ______________________________ capital.
6. Berlin is the ______________________________ capital.
7. Budapest is the ______________________________ capital.
8. Copenhagen is the ______________________________ capital.
9. Bucharest is the ______________________________ capital.

Writing Application: A List

You are a customs officer. Your job is to check the items that people bring into the United States from other countries. Make a list of ten items that you have checked. Use a different proper adjective to describe each item in your list.

Grade 5: Unit 4 Adjectives *(Use with pupil book pages 162–163.)*
Skill: Students will form and use proper adjectives.

Name ______________________________

Choosing Different Adjectives

Late at night, the city is a ~~lonely~~ magical place.

1–10. Complete this post card by filling in each blank with an appropriate adjective from the box. Then compare your post card with a partner's to see how using different adjectives can change the meaning.

exhilarating	terrific	exciting	old
tasty	amazing	terrible	boring
exhausted	famous	long	gooey
busy	tiring	dull	ordinary
awesome	yummy	scenic	dreary

Revising

Dear Chris,

Here we are in __________ New York City.

There are many __________ things to see and do.

Yesterday, we took the ferry to visit the __________ Statue of Liberty.

The walk up to her crown was __________. After that, we visited the

__________ aircraft carrier, *Intrepid*. We ate a __________ dinner in

Chinatown and went to Little Italy for __________ desserts.

Later, we took a __________ carriage ride through Central Park at night.

New York is __________ ! I'm too __________ to write any more.

See you next week. **Brendan**

Name ____________________

1 Correct Sentences

Declarative sentence	A pentagon is a five-sided figure.
Imperative sentence	Please come to Washington.
Interrogative sentence	Is there a pentagon there?
Exclamatory sentence	I can't wait to see it!

A Write each sentence correctly. Separate any run-on sentences.

1. guess the size of the world's largest pentagon

   ____

2. how big is it

   ____

3. this five-sided figure measures about one mile around

   ____

4. take a closer look at the Pentagon Building how huge it is

   ____

B 5–10. Use proofreading marks to correct six sentence errors in this tour guide's script.

Example: do you know how many people work in the Pentagon?

Proofreading

Proofreading Marks
- ¶ Indent
- ^ Add
- Delete
- ≡ Capital letter
- / Small letter

Welcome to the Pentagon?

George E. Bergstrom is the architect who designed the Pentagon. this five-story building covers thirty-four acres. did any of you park in the guest parking lot. That's just one of the parking lots! There are enough parking spaces for 10,000 cars. What a lot of cars.

(continued)

Name ______________________________

1 Correct Sentences *(continued from page 82)*

Challenge

The guide in the cartoons below is giving a tour of the Washington Monument. Write four captions, telling what is happening in these cartoons. Include a declarative sentence, an interrogative sentence, an imperative sentence, and an exclamatory sentence in your captions.

1. 

____

____

3. 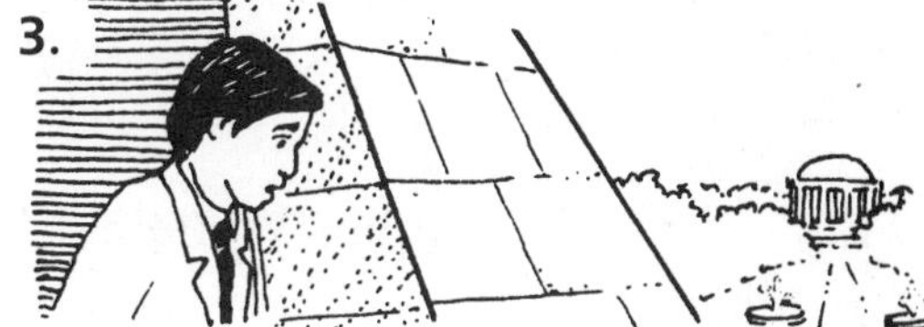

____

____

2. 

____

____

4. 

____

____

Now draw your own cartoon about a tour of a building you know. Write a caption for your cartoon.

Writing Application: A Report

You see a very strange building. What is unusual about it? Write six sentences, describing the building. Include a declarative sentence, an interrogative sentence, an imperative sentence, and an exclamatory sentence in your description.

Name ______________________________

2 Proper Nouns and Adjectives

Proper nouns	Mexico	Taro Suzuki	Friday	Fourth of July
Proper adjectives	Mexican	Swiss	Greek	North American

Find the proper noun or proper adjective in each sentence. Write it correctly.

1. My friend linda mendez has a coin collection. ____________
2. Some coins are from north african countries. ____________
3. One egyptian coin is the size of a quarter. ____________
4. A coin from the people's republic of china has a hole. ____________
5. Recently she bought some ancient greek coins. ____________
6. One has a picture of alexander the great. ____________
7. Last monday she visited a coin exhibit. ____________
8. She spent columbus day at a museum. ____________
9. It was the metropolitan museum of art. ____________
10. The museum featured coins during october. ____________
11. There were displays of old roman coins. ____________
12. Some had been found in the red sea. ____________
13. A few came from ancient spanish ships. ____________
14. The face of julius caesar decorated some. ____________
15. Some showed portraits of caesar augustus. ____________
16. Her trip to new york city was worth the effort. ____________
17. Perhaps someday she will visit london. ____________
18. The british museum has a good collection. ____________
19. The victoria and albert museum also has one. ____________
20. Some coin clubs tour the british isles. ____________

(continued)

Grade 5: Unit 5 Capitalization and Punctuation *(Use with pupil book pages 182–183.)*
Skill: Students will capitalize proper nouns and proper adjectives.

Name ______________________________

2 Proper Nouns and Adjectives *(continued from page 84)*

Challenge

You have been hired to design the money for a new country. Tell about the money by completing the sentences. Use a proper noun or a proper adjective in each answer.

1. The name of the country is ______________________________.
2. The money looks a little like ______________________________ money.
3. The building you work in is called the ______________________________.
4. The person on one bill is named ______________________________.
5. That person is an important ______________________________ citizen.
6. The person on another bill is named ______________________________.

Use the forms below to draw two of the bills that you designed. Include the information given in the sentences that you just completed.

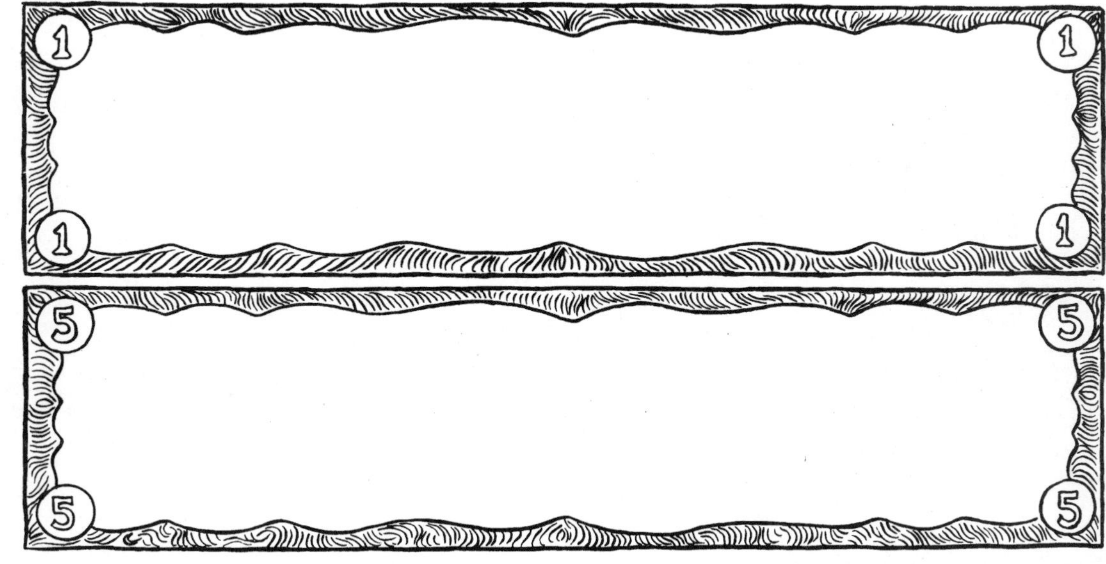

Writing Application: A Diary

Suppose that you are on a trip to a foreign country. Today you exchanged your money, toured a large city, and met a famous person. Write a diary entry, describing your day. Use at least three proper nouns and three proper adjectives.

Name ____________________

3 Commas in a Series

My sister, my brother, and I watched the new family move in.
We introduced ourselves, welcomed them, and invited them for dinner.

A Rewrite each sentence that contains a series. Add commas where they are needed. For each sentence that does not include a series, write *none*.

1. Will Les Martha and Julie be going to our school?

 ____

2. Les will be in the same class as Alfredo and I.

 ____

3. His sisters are in the first third and fourth grades.

 ____

4. Let's invite them to play ball have a picnic swim or sunbathe.

 ____

5. We could meet them at the park in the schoolyard or at my house.

 ____

 ____

B **6–12.** Use proofreading marks to correct the seven comma errors in this invitation.

Example: We must shop, clean, and get dressed for the picnic.

Proofreading
Proofreading Marks
¶ Indent
∧ Add
Delete
≡ Capital letter
/ Small letter
Please Come to Our Party
You are invited to eat swim and have fun. Bring
your pool toys your swimsuit and a towel. We will
pick you up at school at home, or wherever is convenient. The
party is given by Alfredo Michael and Lee.

(continued)

Grade 5: Unit 5 Capitalization and Punctuation *(Use with pupil book pages 184–185.)*
Skill: Students will use commas in a series.

Name ______________________________

3 Commas in a Series (continued from page 86)

Challenge

Read the words written on the chalkboard. Find words and phrases that can be grouped together. Write each group on the lines below.

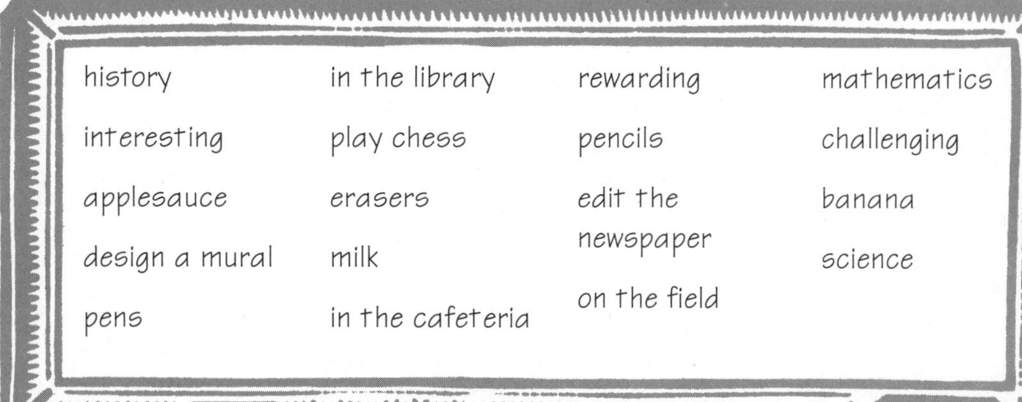

history
interesting
applesauce
design a mural
pens
in the library
play chess
erasers
milk
in the cafeteria
rewarding
pencils
edit the newspaper
on the field
mathematics
challenging
banana
science

1. ______________________
2. ______________________
3. ______________________
4. ______________________
5. ______________________
6. ______________________

Now, on another piece of paper, write six sentences, telling new students about your school. Use each of the above groups of words in a series. Remember to use commas correctly.

Writing Application: A Newsletter

You are writing a neighborhood newsletter. A new family has moved into your neighborhood. Write at least five sentences about who is in the family and what the neighbors are doing to welcome them. Use a series in each of your sentences.

Name ______________________

Writing Sentences with Commas

Several sentences	Band members must attend rehearsals. Band members must practice at home. Band members must perform at school assemblies.
Combined sentence	Band members must attend rehearsals, practice at home, and perform at school assemblies.

Combining Sentences with a Series of Words or Phrases 1–4. Rewrite this paragraph from a music report. Combine each set of underlined sentences to make a series.

Revising

Music is an ancient art form. The very first musical instruments were made of wood. They were also made of animal bone and rock. Prehistoric people may have made music by striking wooden tools together. They may have made music by shaking gourd rattles. They may have made music by clicking stones together. Early flutes were made of hollow reeds. Bones and horns were also made into flutes. Prehistoric people made music to communicate with the gods. Music was also used to communicate with ancestors. Music was used to celebrate a successful hunt. Musical instruments have changed, but music remains an important part of many cultures.

____

____

____

____

____

____

____

____

____

(continued)

Grade 5: Unit 5 Capitalization and Punctuation *(Use with pupil book pages 186–187.)*
Skill: Students will combine sentences to make a series.

Name ______________________________

Writing Sentences with Commas *(continued from page 88)*

Several sentences	To play the flute take a deep breath. To play the flute blow through the mouthpiece. Cover some of the holes with your fingers.
Combined sentence	To play the flute take a deep breath, blow through the mouthpiece, and cover some of the holes with your fingers.

Combining Whole Sentences in a Series 5–8. Rewrite each advertisement by combining sentences to form a series. Remember to choose conjunctions that fit the meaning of your sentences, such as *and* and *or.*

Revising

5. The choir could sing a melody. The brass section could play a fanfare. The violinist could perform a solo.

6. Our rock band is looking for a drummer. The bass guitarist needs a place to practice. The lead singer wants to find a vocal coach.

7. Our school needs a music director. The drama department needs a rehearsal pianist. Our after-school program needs a piano teacher.

8. Place your musical ad here. Get three months for the price of two. Pay by cash to get an additional month free.

____

____

____

____

____

____

____

____

____

Name ____________________

4 More Uses for Commas

Introductory words	Oh, I heard about your class. Yes, it's great!
Nouns in direct address	Elsa, come to my class with me. You will enjoy it, Elsa. You will see, Elsa, that it is useful.

Rewrite each sentence, adding commas where they are needed.

1. Yolanda I hear that you're taking a course in first aid.

____

2. Yes Willy I'm taking a course with Ms. Liang.

____

3. Can you tell me more about the course Yolanda?

____

4. Well Willy I've only had one class.

____

5. I wonder Yolanda if it's too late for me to sign up.

____

6. No I don't believe it is.

____

7. Why don't you come with me Willy?

____

8. Oh Ms. Liang let me introduce you to Willy.

____

9. Well you're just in time Willy to help with a demonstration.

____

10. Yolanda help me put Willy's arm in this sling.

____

(continued)

Name ___________________________

4 More Uses for Commas (continued from page 90)

Challenge

Study the cartoons below. Think of a story that will fit the pictures. Write what each character is saying. Use an introductory word or a noun in direct address in each speech balloon. Remember to use commas correctly.

Now draw your own cartoon on another piece of paper. Use an introductory word or a noun in direct address in each speech balloon.

Writing Application: A Note

You know someone who is in the hospital. Write a note to wish that person a speedy recovery. Use the person's name at least three times in your note. Use the introductory words *oh, yes, well,* and *no* at least once. Remember to use commas correctly.

Name ______________________________

Writing Sentences with Commas

Two sentences	She was trying to protect the forests. Julia Hill was hoping to change a company's viewpoint.
Combined sentence	Trying to protect the forests, Julia Hill was hoping to change a company's viewpoint.

Combining Sentences: Introductory Groups of Words 1–4. Revise the news story below. Combine each pair of underlined sentences by changing one sentence into an introductory phrase.

Revising

She was living in a tree for more than two years. Julia Butterfly Hill protested logging in northern California. Her tree-house home was a large platform high above the forest floor. She was settling an agreement with Pacific Lumber Company. Julia came down from the ancient redwood tree. She smiled as she descended. Her walking was wobbly. The lumber company is saving Julia's tree and the area around it. They will receive $50,000 from Julia and the environmentalists. The payment is for Pacific Lumber's lost income. They are accepting the money. The logging company will then donate the same amount to a state university for forestry studies.

____

____

____

____

____

____

____

____

____

____

____

(continued)

Grade 5: Unit 5 Capitalization and Punctuation *(Use with pupil book pp. 190–191.)*
Skill: Students will combine sentences by changing one sentence into an introductory phrase.

Name ______________________________

Writing Sentences with Commas *(continued from page 92)*

Two sentences	Jason read the article about Julia Hill in the newspaper. He wrote her a letter.
Combined sentence	After Jason read the article about Julia Hill in the newspaper, he wrote her a letter.

Common Subordinating Conjunctions				
after	as	before	since	when
although	because	if	until	while

Combining Sentences: Introductory Groups of Words 5–8. Rewrite Jason's letter to Julia Hill. Combine each pair of underlined sentences, using a subordinating conjunction from the box that fits the meaning.

Revising

Dear Ms. Hill,

I read about you in the newspaper. I did some research. The logging companies are allowed to destroy the forests. Wild animals will have nowhere to live. We must stop the destruction of the planet's forests. I am too young to protest by living in a redwood tree. I am donating half of my allowance to environmental causes. I have decided to study environmental law. I plan to be an environmental lawyer. I can help with the important work you are doing.

Sincerely,
Jason Simon

____

____

____

____

____

____

____

____

Name ______________________________

5 Interjections

Hey! Try to find some good seats.
Oh, the balloon rally is starting!

Complete each line of this skit, using the interjection in parentheses. Use the correct punctuation after each interjection.

1. Safa: ____________ The colors are fantastic! **(Great)**
2. Lois: ____________ That green one is the highest. **(Wow)**
3. Willy: ____________ what a beautiful sight! **(Ah)**
4. Lois: ____________ Hot-air ballooning might be fun. **(Hey)**
5. Safa: ____________ It's too early in the morning. **(Good grief)**
6. Willy: ____________ it's less windy in the morning. **(Well)**
7. Safa: ____________ a strong wind could be dangerous! **(Oh)**
8. Lois: ____________ Look at the tiny baskets! **(Ha)**
9. Willy: ____________ There are two people in each basket. **(Goodness)**
10. Safa: ____________ a larger balloon carries even more weight! **(Well)**
11. Lois: ____________ One balloon is descending early! **(Oops)**
12. Willy: ____________ It landed safely. **(Whew)**
13. Safa: ____________ guess who the first balloonists were! **(Hey)**
14. Lois: ____________ Is this a joke? **(Oh, no)**
15. Safa: ____________ a duck, a sheep, and a rooster were the first! **(Ha)**
16. Willy: ____________ That's a good one! **(Cheers)**
17. Lois: ____________ I don't believe it. **(Well)**
18. Safa: ____________ It *is* true! **(Hey)**

(continued)

Grade 5: Unit 5 Capitalization and Punctuation *(Use with pupil book pages 192–193.)*
Skill: Students will use commas and exclamation points to punctuate interjections.

Name ______________________________

5 Interjections *(continued from page 94)*

Challenge

The characters in the cartoon are hot-air ballooning. Tell what each character is saying about the view down below. Write a sentence in each speech balloon. Begin each one with an interjection. Use the correct punctuation after each interjection.

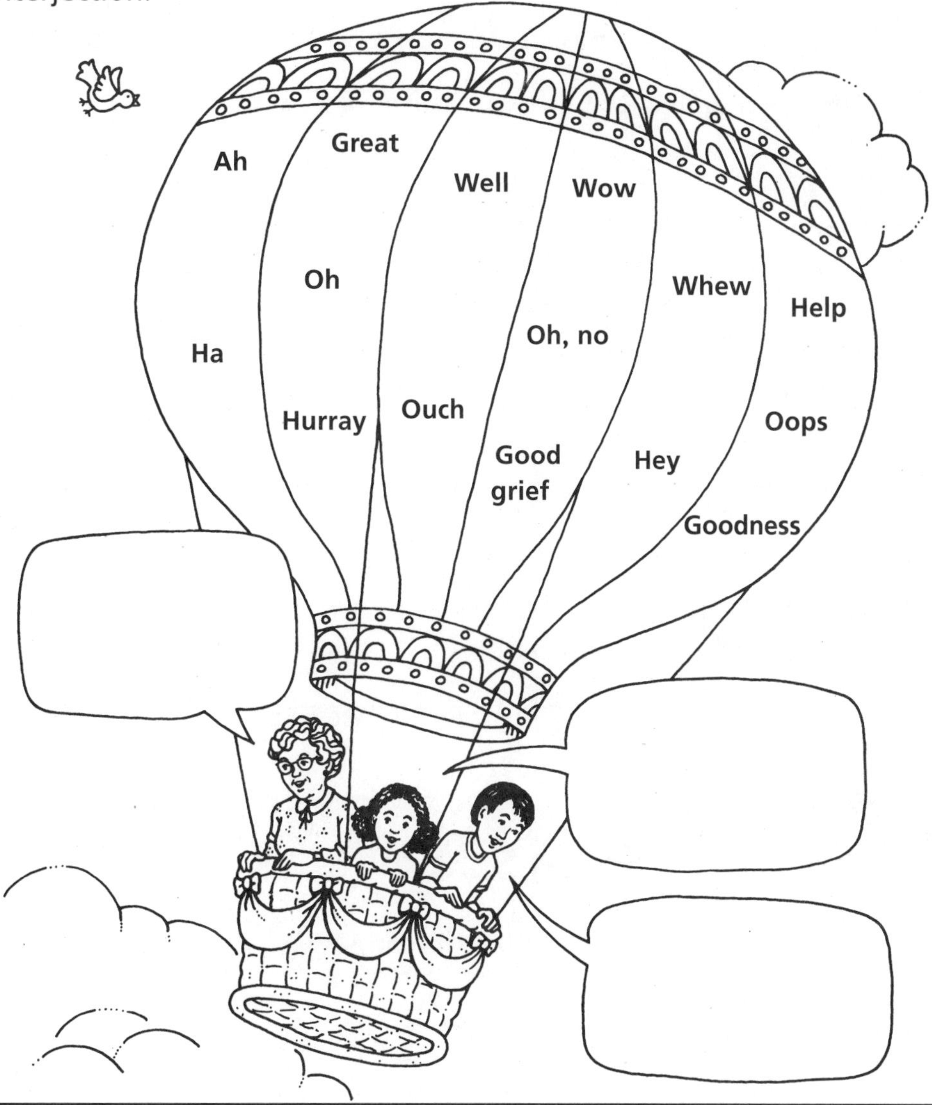

Ah
Great
Well
Wow
Oh
Whew
Help
Ha
Oh, no
Hurray
Ouch
Oops
Good grief
Hey
Goodness

Writing Application: A Skit

You and a friend are discussing a rubber raft trip that you have recently taken. Write a skit, using interjections to show feeling or emotion. Remember to use either an exclamation point or a comma after each interjection.

Name ____________________

6 Quotations

> The firefighter exclaimed, "Fire safety is important!"
> "You should know what to do in case of fire," she added.
> "There are rules," she explained, "that you should follow."
> "You must know some," she said. "Can you remember them?"

A Rewrite each sentence, using punctuation marks and capital letters correctly.

1. the firefighter announced there are rules for fire safety

____

2. let's see if you know what they are she added

____

3. should electrical wiring Mark asked be checked carefully

____

4. never overload an electrical outlet Judy exclaimed

____

B **5–10.** Use proofreading marks to correct six errors in punctuation and capital letters in this school newspaper story.

Example: The firefighter said,"don't stack newspapers, rags, or paints."

Proofreading Marks

- ¶ Indent
- ∧ Add
- Delete
- ≡ Capital letter
- / Small letter

Tipton School News

Local Fire Breaks Out!

Last week there was a fire at the home of student Karen Howard. When asked about the fire, Principal Tobin said this is a terrible disaster for Karen. Her family lost nearly everything. Mr. Tobin added it was good no one was hurt.

(continued)

Grade 5: Unit 5 Capitalization and Punctuation *(Use with pupil book pages 194–195.)*
Skill: Students will capitalize and will punctuate direct quotations.

Name ______________________________

6 Quotations *(continued from page 96)*

Challenge

The students below drew posters to illustrate their reports on school fire drills. Use the posters to help you decide what each student is saying about fire safety. Then write a direct quotation for each picture.

1. 

____

____

2. 

____

____

3. 

____

____

4. 

____

____

5. 

____

____

6. 

____

____

Writing Application: A Dialogue

You and a friend are having a conversation about fire safety. Your friend is asking you about safety precautions you take in your home, and you are answering. Write the dialogue, using direct quotations. Remember to use capital letters and punctuation marks correctly.

Name ______________________

7 Abbreviations

Titles	Mister	**Mr.**	Junior	**Jr.**
	a married woman	**Mrs.**	Senior	**Sr.**
	any woman	**Ms.**	Doctor	**Dr.**
Businesses	Corporation	**Corp.**	Limited	**Ltd.**
Days	Tuesday	**Tues.**	Sunday	**Sun.**
Months	February	**Feb.**	August	**Aug.**
Addresses	Apartment	**Apt.**	Route	**Rte.**
States	California	**CA**	Illinois	**IL**
Initials	Susan Gloria	**S. G.**	Ling Chow	**L. C.**

A Write these groups of words, using the correct abbreviations and initials.

1. Audio Service Corporation ______________________
2. Wednesday, September 29, 1875 ______________________
3. Alva John Holmes Senior ______________________
4. Rodriguez, Incorporated ______________________
5. Friday, August 13, 1990 ______________________

B Write these addresses. Use the correct abbreviations and initials for the underlined words.

6. Doctor Jane Wilbur ______________________
   Route 30 ______________________
   Richmond, Virginia 23219 ______________________
7. Four Star Company, Limited ______________________
   Post Office Box 5555 ______________________
   Dallas, Texas 75234 ______________________
8. Mister Alonso Richard Amanda ______________________
   2001 Brentwood Avenue ______________________
   Springfield, Illinois 62704 ______________________

(continued)

Name ___________________________________

7 Abbreviations *(continued from page 98)*

Challenge

Use the code in the chart below to solve the puzzles. First, find the abbreviation for each state in the numbered list. Then write the letter the abbreviation stands for above the number of the state. The first one has been done for you.

CA	NY	TX	OR	IN	AL	DE	WA	VT	TN	ND	AK	IL
A	B	C	D	E	F	G	H	I	J	K	L	M
OH	**NM**	**GA**	**NE**	**FL**	**MI**	**CT**	**ME**	**CO**	**MO**	**SC**	**VA**	**KY**
N	O	P	Q	R	S	T	U	V	W	X	Y	Z

1. California
2. New York
3. New York
4. Florida
5. Indiana
6. Colorado
7. Vermont
8. California
9. Connecticut
10. Vermont
11. New Mexico
12. Ohio
13. Michigan
14. Texas
15. California
16. Ohio
17. New York
18. Indiana
19. Alabama
20. Maine
21. Ohio

A
___ ___ ___ ___ ___ ___ ___ ___ ___ ___ ___ ___ ___
1 2 3 4 5 6 7 8 9 10 11 12 13

___ ___ ___   ___ ___   ___ ___ ___!
14 15 16   17 18   19 20 21

Now solve this puzzle. Use the same code.

1. Virginia
2. New Mexico
3. Maine
4. California
5. Florida
6. Indiana
7. California
8. Texas
9. New Mexico
10. Oregon
11. Indiana
12. New York
13. Florida
14. Indiana
15. California
16. North Dakota
17. Indiana
18. Florida

___ ___ ___   ___ ___ ___
1 2 3   4 5 6

___   ___ ___ ___ ___   ___ ___ ___ ___ ___ ___ ___!
7   8 9 10 11   12 13 14 15 16 17 18

Writing Application: An Invitation

Write an invitation to invite your aunt to a school play. Include the date, the time of the play, and the address of your school. Use at least five abbreviations.

Name ________________________________

8 Titles

I read the book <u>The **P**rince and the **P**auper</u>.
I read <u>The **D**aily **S**tar</u> every morning.
The chorus sang **"H**ome on the **R**ange.**"**
We read the poem **"T**he **S**ong of the **D**esert.**"**

A Write each sentence correctly.

1. Today's parktown crier, our newspaper, contained lots of information.

____

2. Joanna read a review of the book called the black stallion.

____

3. She is now reading the chapter called homeward bound.

____

4. Tod saw a review of the movie chariots of fire.

____

B **5–12.** Use proofreading marks to correct eight capitalization and punctuation errors in the titles in the list.

Example: I like to play "the star spangled banner" on the piano.

Proofreading Marks
- ¶ Indent
- ∧ Add
- Delete
- ≡ Capital letter
- / Small letter

What I Did Last Summer

- Read an article titled things to do on vacation
- Wrote a letter to the editor of a magazine called Cobblestone
- Read the book *What's the big idea, Ben Franklin?*
- Wrote a story titled The Mystery of the Missing Lunch

(continued)

Grade 5: Unit 5 Capitalization and Punctuation *(Use with pupil book pages 198–199.)*
Skill: Students will capitalize and will punctuate titles.

Name ______________________________

8 Titles (continued from page 100)

Challenge

You are the editor of your school newspaper. Below is a layout for the front page of the paper. Each block contains a brief description of a story. Write a name for the newspaper in the top space. Then think of a title for each story. Write the title above the description of the story.

VOL. XXIX ★ ★ ★ ★ ★ MARCH 21, 2003		
____________________	____________________	____________________
____________________	____________________	____________________
a poem about homework	a short story about a mountain-climbing expedition	an article about the crowded conditions in the cafeteria
____________________	____________________	____________________
____________________	____________________	____________________
a review of a new magazine for teenagers	a movie review	a book review

Now, on another piece of paper, write a report to your teacher, telling about the subject of each article. Write six sentences. Include the title of a poem, a magazine, a short story, an article, a movie, or a book in each sentence.

Writing Application: A Letter

Your pen pal has asked you to recommend some books and movies. Write a letter to your pen pal, recommending your favorite book, short story, magazine, movie, poem, and song. Be sure to write the titles correctly.

Name ______________________

1 Subject Pronouns

Nouns	Subject Pronouns
Manuel and Judy heard a speech.	**They** heard a speech.
The speaker was Mrs. Ruiz.	The speaker was **she**.

Write the subject pronoun that could replace the underlined word or words.

1. Manuel, Judy, and I have been reading about dinosaurs. ________
2. Dinosaurs became extinct millions of years ago. ________
3. The best-informed student is Manuel. ________
4. Judy and Manuel read about the brontosaur. ________
5. The brontosaur was one of the largest dinosaurs. ________
6. How large was this dinosaur? ________
7. Judy and I made a chart. ________
8. The chart gave a description of several dinosaurs. ________
9. The allosaurus and the stegosaur were included. ________
10. Judy showed the chart to Mrs. Ruiz and Mr. Li. ________
11. The science teacher is Mrs. Ruiz. ________
12. Mr. Li is an expert on dinosaurs. ________
13. A recent speaker at the science fair was Mr. Li. ________
14. The science fair was visited by several paleontologists. ________
15. Paleontologists are scientists who study fossils. ________
16. Fossils are prints found in rocks. ________
17. Judy and I learned a great deal from these scientists. ________
18. The person who was most impressed by the fair was Judy. ________
19. Next week Judy will visit the Museum of Natural History. ________
20. The museum has a wonderful display of dinosaur skeletons. ________

(continued)

Name ______________________________

1 Subject Pronouns *(continued from page 102)*

Challenge

Melissa Spencer and several other scientists have uncovered the skeleton of an enormous dinosaur. Melissa wants to telegraph her college to tell about her discovery. However, her message is too long. Rewrite the message, replacing nouns with subject pronouns. Make sure the message still makes sense.

WESTERN TELEGRAPH TELEGRAM

The other scientists and Melissa Spencer found the skeleton of a dinosaur STOP Melissa and the scientists think that the dinosaur weighed one hundred tons STOP The dinosaur was probably one hundred twenty feet long STOP Several bones have already been uncovered STOP These bones still must be cleaned and identified STOP Melissa will be forwarding photographs of this discovery immediately STOP

Melissa Spencer

____

____

____

____

____

____

On a sheet of paper, figure out the cost of the original telegram. There is a charge of $8.75 for the first ten words and $.45 for each additional word. Do not count the word STOP or Melissa's signature. Figure out the cost of the rewritten telegram and how much Melissa could save by using pronouns.

Original Telegram: __________ **Rewritten Telegram:** __________

Savings: __________

Writing Application: Story

You and your friends suddenly find yourselves living in the time of the dinosaurs. Write a paragraph about what you see, using five subject pronouns.

Name ____________________

2 Object Pronouns

Nouns	Object Pronouns
The Kents welcomed Fern. Fern went with the Kents.	The Kents welcomed **her**. Fern went with **them**.
Subject Pronoun	**Object Pronoun**
It was an interesting tour.	Fern liked **it**.

Rewrite these sentences, using the correct pronouns.

1. Mr. and Mrs. Kent gave Fern and (I, me) a tour of the bee farm.

   ____

2. This was the first visit for (she, her) and (I, me).

   ____

3. Mr. Kent told (we, us) that beekeepers are called apiculturists.

   ____

4. (I, Me) asked (he, him) why beekeepers wear such strange clothing.

   ____

5. The clothes protect (they, them) from bee stings.

   ____

6. The Kents put beekeepers' veils on (we, us).

   ____

7. (We, Us) followed (he, him) and (she, her) into the field.

   ____

8. Mrs. Kent cautioned Fern and (I, me) to move slowly.

   ____

9. (She, Her) explained to (we, us) that bees are social insects.

   ____

10. (We, Us) watched (they, them) communicate by dancing.

   ____

(continued)

Grade 5: Unit 6 Pronouns *(Use with pupil book pages 218–219.)*
Skill: Students will choose subject and object pronouns to complete sentences.

Name ______________________________

2 Object Pronouns *(continued from page 104)*

Challenge

Mr. Kent has decided to post signs around the beehives, warning visitors about possible dangers. Help Mr. Kent by writing four warning sentences. Include at least one object pronoun in each warning.

1. WARNING!

____
____
____
____

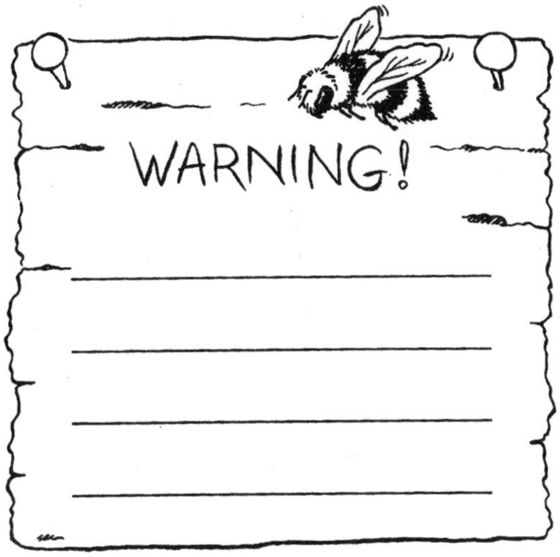

2. WARNING!

____
____
____
____

3. WARNING!

____
____
____
____

4. WARNING!

____
____
____
____

Writing Application: An Advertisement

You work in the advertising department of a book publishing company. Your assignment is to write an advertisement for a new book about bees. Tell why the book would be interesting to beekeepers, students, and scientists. Use subject and object pronouns in your advertisement. Underline the subject pronouns once and the object pronouns twice.

Name ______________________________

3 Using *I* and *me*

Ella and **I** enjoy photography.	**I** enjoy photography.
Dad shows his photos to Ella and **me**.	Dad shows his photos to **me.**

A Rewrite each sentence, using the correct word or words in parentheses.

1. Ella and (I, me) went to a photography show.

____

2. It was an interesting experience for Ella and (I, me).

____

3. Dad decided not to go with Ella and (I, me).

____

4. Ella and (I, me) took the bus.

____

B **5–8.** Use proofreading marks to correct four incorrect uses of *I* and *me* in this journal entry.

Example: The guide at the show spoke to Ella and ~~I~~ me.

Proofreading Marks

- ¶ Indent
- ∧ Add
- Delete
- ≡ Capital letter
- / Small letter

October 2

Today Ella and me went to the museum. She and I saw photographs by the famous photographer Ansel Adams. The museum guide gave me and Ella a short tour. He explained to her and I that Ansel Adams wanted to preserve the wilderness. Ella and I wrote comments in the visitor's book. The guide asked her and me who wrote "Great pictures" in the book. I said, "It was me."

(continued)

Name ______________________________

3 Using *I* and *me* (continued from page 106)

Challenge

Underline the correct pronoun in parentheses to complete each riddle. Then write the answer to each riddle.

1. (I, Me) have holes on my sides. You put (I, me) in a camera. You need the camera and (I, me) to take photographs.
I am ____________________.

2. You can find my friends and (I, me) in museums. Sometimes (I, me) am black and white. Sometimes people take (I, me) with color film.
I am a ____________________.

3. Sometimes (I, me) am made of leather. (I, Me) have a strap. You can carry a camera in (I, me).
I am a ____________________.

4. Sometimes (I, me) am made of metal. (I, Me) have three legs. You use (I, me) to steady a camera.
I am a ____________________.

5. (I, Me) am made of paper. You can display photographs in (I, me). (I, Me) usually have a hard cover.
I am a ____________________.

6. (I, Me) am a place. There are no lights in (I, me). You can develop photographs in (I, me).
I am a ____________________.

Now, on another piece of paper, write two riddles of your own. Use the pronoun *I* or *me* in each sentence.

Writing Application: A Personal Narrative

Write about a trip you have taken with a friend. Write at least five sentences, telling where you went and what you saw. Use *I* or *me* in each sentence.

Name ______________________________

4 Possessive Pronouns

Before Nouns	Stand Alone
Her book is interesting.	The interesting book is **hers.**
My book is long.	**Mine** is long.

A Rewrite each sentence, using the correct possessive pronoun in parentheses.

1. Today (our, ours) school is sponsoring a book fair.

____

2. Has (your, yours) ever had such an event?

____

3. Actually (my, mine) teacher suggested the idea.

____

4. The idea of inviting famous authors was also (her, hers).

____

B **5–8.** Use proofreading marks to correct four possessive pronoun errors in this letter.

Example: After the book fair, I will give you ~~mine~~ ^my comments.

Proofreading

Proofreading Marks

- ¶ Indent
- ∧ Add
- ⌇ Delete
- ≡ Capital letter
- / Small letter

Dear Aunt May,

Last week was a special one for mine school. We had two famous authors talk about theirs works. Steven Kellogg talked about his books. Then Peggy Parish read from novels of her. *Key to the Treasure* is a good book she read to ours classes. My job was to take the authors from room to room.

Your nephew, Kareem

(continued)

Grade 5: Unit 6 Pronouns *(Use with pupil book pages 222–223.)*
Skill: Students will choose possessive pronouns to complete sentences.

Name ______________________________

4 Possessive Pronouns *(continued from page 108)*

Challenge

Find out what type of book each student enjoys reading. Use the clues below the chart to help you find the answers. Place an X under each category that you eliminate. Then draw a star in the box that shows what type of book each student likes best.

	Legend	Biography	Mystery	Science
Lee				
Bonnie				
Maria				
Seth				

Clues

- No person's name begins with the same letter as his or her favorite book.
- Bonnie and Seth don't enjoy works of fiction.
- Lee and Maria don't like books that are nonfiction.

Now write a sentence that tells about each person's favorite type of book. Use a possessive pronoun in each sentence.

1. Lee: ______________________________
2. Bonnie: ______________________________
3. Maria: ______________________________
4. Seth: ______________________________
5. Bonnie and Seth: ______________________________
6. Lee and Maria: ______________________________

Writing Application: A Report

You and your friends are setting up a library for the younger children in your neighborhood. Write at least five sentences that tell what books you will have and who will donate the books. Use at least five different possessive pronouns.

Name ______________________________

Writing with Pronouns

Noun Overload	Improved with Pronouns
Sonja Henie was a famous ice skater. Sonja Henie won the world championship ten times. Sonja Henie won many gold medals in the Olympics. Sonja Henie was a great champion.	Sonja Henie was a famous ice skater. **She** won the world championship ten times. **She** won many gold medals in the Olympics. Sonja Henie was a great champion.

Using Enough Pronouns 1–2. Rewrite these Olympic profiles. In each paragraph, use the correct pronouns to replace nouns that are repeated too often.

Revising

Some people believe that Jim Thorpe was the greatest athlete in the world. At the 1912 Olympics, Jim Thorpe won the pentathlon and decathlon events. Jim Thorpe went on to play Major League Baseball, and Jim Thorpe also played professional football.

Wilma Rudolph overcame great hardship. As a child, Wilma Rudolph was very ill. Wilma Rudolph's doctors said that she would never walk again. Wilma Rudolph went on to win three gold medals in track and field.

1. ______________________________

____

____

____

2. ______________________________

____

____

____

(continued)

Name ______________________________

Writing with Pronouns *(continued from page 110)*

Unclear	Our town has an ice rink. Grace is practicing for a skating competition. It is always crowded after school.
Clear	Our town has an ice rink. Grace is practicing for a skating competition. **The rink** is always crowded after school.

Writing Clearly with Pronouns 3–8. This magazine story introduction has pronouns that are used too much and used unclearly. Rewrite the introduction by replacing the underlined pronouns with nouns.

Revising

Figure-skating specials sprinkle the winter TV airwaves like snowflakes. They combine athletics and art for viewers to enjoy. They are tuning in more and more often.

The International Skating Union now allows amateur skaters to skate in ice shows. They can skate in holiday ice shows or TV competitions. Some of them feature both professionals and amateurs. Skating appears on TV more than ever before. Its popularity continues to grow even in a non-Olympic year.

Many skaters thought their careers were over after they won a gold medal. They were wrong. You can see many of them in "Stars on Ice."

Name ___________________________

5 Contractions with Pronouns

Pronoun + Verb	Contraction	Pronoun + Verb	Contraction
I am	I'm	we would	we'd
it is	it's	I have	I've
you are	you're	he has	he's
I will	I'll	you had	you'd

A Write the contractions that can be made from the underlined words.

1. I have always liked big cats as much as Kim does. ____________
2. She is reading about lions and tigers now. ____________
3. She has purchased many posters of leopards and panthers. ____________
4. We are going to see an exhibit about big cats. ____________
5. I am impressed with their strength and grace. ____________
6. I will take pictures of the exhibit. ____________
7. You may come with us if you would like. ____________
8. The speaker will discuss the cats that we have read about. ____________
9. He will tell about the spotted members of the cat family. ____________

B **10–14.** There are five incorrect contractions in this tour guide's presentation. Use proofreading marks to correct them.

Example: ~~Its~~ **It's** interesting to see the tigers at the zoo.

Proofreading Marks

- ¶ Indent
- ∧ Add
- Delete
- ≡ Capital letter
- / Small letter

Proofreading

Ladies and gentlemen, the zoo tour can start if youll just get in line. First, we'll be visiting the cougars. Theyr'e also known as mountain lions and pumas. We can see Ms. Bikila getting ready to feed them. Shes holding a pan of raw meat and bones. Youl'l be surprised to know that wild cougars live in many parts of North and South America. Lets move on to the tigers.

(continued)

Name ______________________________

5 Contractions with Pronouns *(continued from page 112)*

Challenge

Below are pictures that you took of big cats during a trip to Africa and Asia. Write a caption, telling what is happening in each picture. Each caption should be a complete sentence. The sentences can be humorous or factual. Use a different contraction in each sentence.

LIONS

1. 

____

2. 

____

LEOPARDS AND JAGUARS

3. 

____

4. 

____

TIGERS

5. 

____

6. 

____

Writing Application: A Diary

You have been on a trip to Africa. While you were there, you photographed many wild animals. Write a diary entry about your adventures. Include at least five contractions that are made from pronouns and verbs.

Name ___________________________________

6 Double Subjects

Incorrect	These **animals they** lived long ago.
Correct	These **animals** lived long ago.
	They lived long ago.

Rewrite each sentence, correcting the double subject.

1. Poco and Marie they were collecting rocks for a science project.

2. Marie she found a piece of shiny black rock.

3. Poco he studied the piece carefully.

4. The rock it contained the print of a fish.

5. The print it is called a fossil.

6. Fossils they tell about the past.

7. Sometimes animal bones or shells they turn to stone.

8. This process it takes millions of years.

9. Poco he was impressed by Marie's discovery.

10. Later, Marie she showed the class the fossil.

(continued)

Grade 5: Unit 6 Pronouns *(Use with pupil book pages 228–229.)*
Skill: Students will correct double subjects.

Name ______________________________

6 Double Subjects *(continued from page 114)*

Challenge

A paleontologist, a scientist who studies fossils, is a kind of detective. You, too, can be a detective. Use the words on each fossil to make a sentence. There is one extra word on each fossil. Cross out that word. Then rewrite the correct sentence on the line.

1. like somewhat mammoths elephants the they Asian and African looked

____

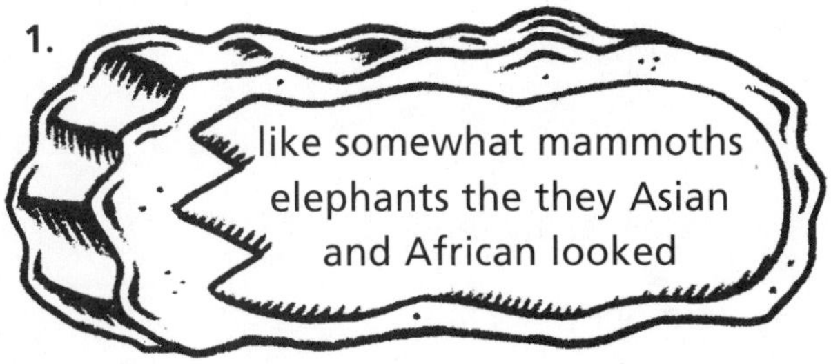

2. made years unusual an scientist he a ago discovery several

____

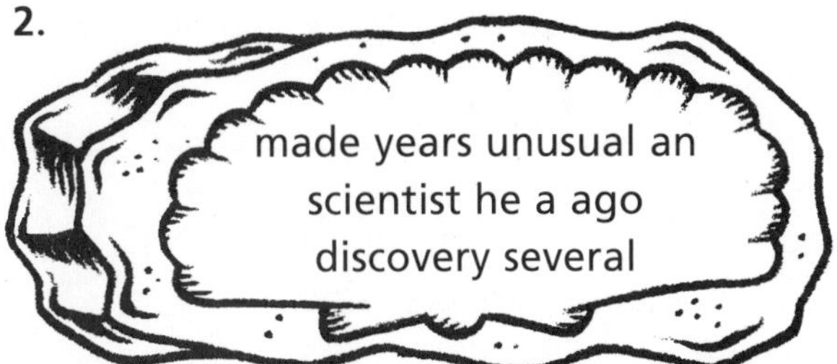

3. found it frozen an the in ground mammoth was ancient

____

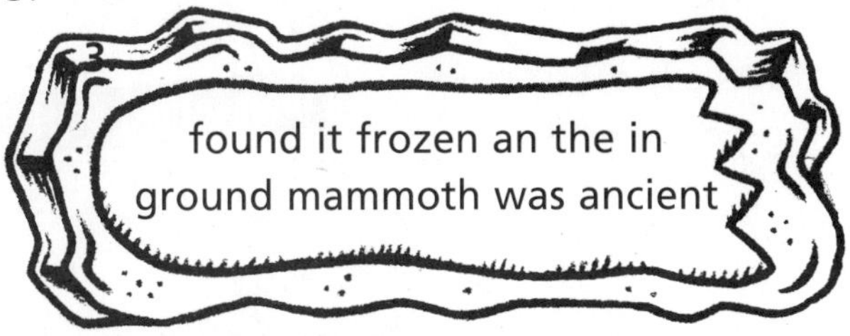

4. animal's blades still mouth they of were grass the in

____

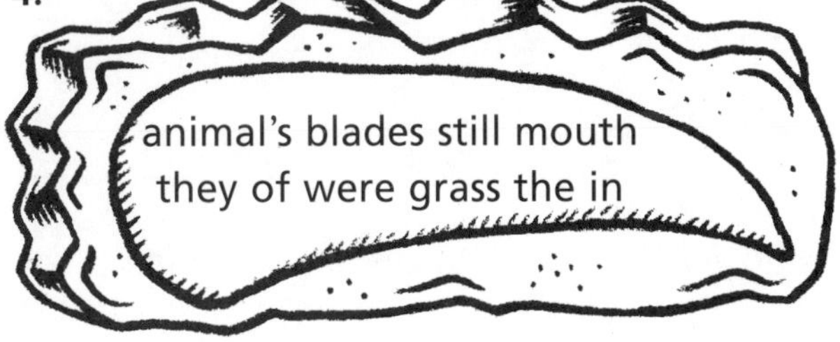

Writing Application: A Science Report

You are a rock in the forest. You have been there thousands of years. Write a description of some of the people, the animals, or the plants that you have seen. Do not use any double subjects in your description.

Name ____________________

7 Using *we* and *us* with Nouns

We students have a problem.	Those with no money are **we** children.
Dad gave **us** boys a lecture.	He often talks to **us** children about money.

A Write *we* or *us* to complete each sentence correctly.

1. Sports equipment is expensive for __________ athletes.
2. __________ artists always seem to need paint supplies.
3. The biggest spenders are __________ students who are interested in fashion.
4. Obviously __________ spenders never have any money.
5. __________ children must earn some money.
6. Earning money does not come easily to __________ young people.
7. Those who have money will be __________ workers.
8. Selling plants is a possibility for __________ gardeners.
9. Neighbors will also give __________ students some business.
10. Drivers will hire __________ car washers.

B **11–15.** Use proofreading marks to correct five errors in the use of *we* and *us* in the following poster.

Example: You can trust ~~we~~ us students to do the work.

Proofreading

For Hire

Do you have work for we students to do? You can hire we kids for reasonable rates. The workers who work together to get big jobs done are us students. We hard workers will save you time and money. How can us students help you? Our customers are pleased because us workers are dependable. You will be pleased too.

(continued)

Name ______________________________

7 Using *we* and *us* with Nouns (continued from page 116)

Challenge

You and a group of your friends have decided to start your own companies. To attract customers, you will distribute fliers to your friends and neighbors. Describe your qualifications and the services you will provide. Write three sentences for each flier below. Use *we* or *us* with a noun in each sentence.

1. Dog-sitting by Carrie and Steve

____

____

____

2. ANDY and RANDY'S CAR WASH

WASH +WAX $15

WASH $5

____

____

____

3. CUTTER'S LANDSCAPING SERVICE

____

____

____

Writing Application: A Persuasive Article

You and your classmates want to raise money to buy new sports equipment for your team. Write five sentences, telling what you and the other students will do to earn that money. In each sentence, use the pronoun *we* or *us* with a noun.

Name ______________________________

Using Homophones Correctly

Did you (sea, see) any lettuce at the store?
Did you **see** any lettuce at the store?

1–10. This kitchen note has 10 incorrect homophones. Cross out each mistake and write the correct homophone above it. Use the chart below to help you.

Homophone	Meaning	Homophone	Meaning
ate	did eat	their	belongs to them
eight	number 8	they're	they are
it's	it is	flour	milled grain
its	belongs to it	flower	a bloom
doe	female deer	sum	total in math
dough	uncooked bread	some	not all
grate	grind into small pieces	buy	to purchase
		by	near
great	terrific	way	direction
won	did win	weigh	put on a scale
one	number 1		

Revising

By won pound of hamburger. Get at least ate potatoes. Don't forget flower for making bread doe. Get apples and have the checker way them carefully. Its unfair being overcharged. Look for hot dogs—their in the meat case. Oh, and get sum special ice cream. Let's have a grate dessert.

Grammar

Name ______________________________

1 Adverbs

How	The artist painted **carefully.**
When	**Soon** she displayed her work.
Where	Her paintings hung **there.**

A Underline the adverb in each sentence. Then write whether the adverb tells *how, when,* or *where.*

1. Anna Mary Robertson always helped her mother. ____________
2. She patiently took care of the younger children. ____________
3. Then she became a housekeeper. ____________
4. Her employers lived nearby. ____________
5. A hired man worked there with her. ____________

B Write the adverb in each sentence. Then draw an arrow from the adverb in the sentence to the verb that it describes.

6. Eventually Anna Mary married the man, Thomas Moses. ____________
7. Anna and Tom worked hard. ____________
8. They successfully ran a dairy business. ____________
9. Later Anna began painting. ____________
10. The eighty-year-old artist worked inside. ____________
11. Her bedroom studio was upstairs. ____________
12. Anna remembered her childhood vividly. ____________
13. She skillfully used a primitive style of painting. ____________
14. Her paintings sold well. ____________
15. Soon critics referred to her as Grandma Moses. ____________
16. Exhibitors displayed her paintings everywhere. ____________

(continued)

Name ______________________________

1 Adverbs *(continued from page 119)*

Challenge

Artists use colors when they paint pictures, but writers use words. You can use describing words, such as adverbs, to "paint a picture" or to create an image. The adverbs you choose make the picture clearer. On the paint cans below, list adverbs that tell *how, when,* and *where.*

Now use these adverbs to write five different sentences. For each sentence, add two different adverbs to the short sentence below. Notice how the meaning of each sentence and the picture you have created change when you use different adverbs.

The artist painted.

Example: **Yesterday** the artist painted **indoors**.

1. ______________________________
2. ______________________________
3. ______________________________
4. ______________________________
5. ______________________________

Writing Application: A Personal Narrative

Think of something that you do well. Your special talent could be in art, in sports, in science, or in some other field. Write a paragraph about your special talent. Use adverbs that tell *how, when,* and *where.*

Name ______________________________

Writing with Adverbs

Sentences Without Adverbs	Sentences Elaborated With Adverbs
The tour was over.	The tour was over **early**.
It ended.	It ended **here**.
The tour guide broke her leg.	The tour guide **accidentally** broke her leg.

Elaborating Sentences 1–8. Rewrite this e-mail message. Elaborate each underlined sentence by adding adverbs that tell *when, where,* or *how*.

Revising e-mail

To: Dad
From: Chris
Subject: Arrival

I changed my flight. I will arrive on Tuesday. I hope that you can come to the airport. Please meet me. I have a lot of luggage. I bought many souvenirs. I spent all of my money! However, I found something for everyone. Some of it is breakable and needs to be carried. I'm glad to be coming home. See you at the airport!

____

____

____

____

____

____

____

____

____

____

____

____

(continued)

Name ______________________________

Writing with Adverbs *(continued from page 121)*

Two sentences	The campers sang. They were loud.
Combined sentence	The campers sang **loudly**.

Combining Sentences 9–15. Rewrite this post card. Combine each set of underlined sentences, using adverbs.

Revising

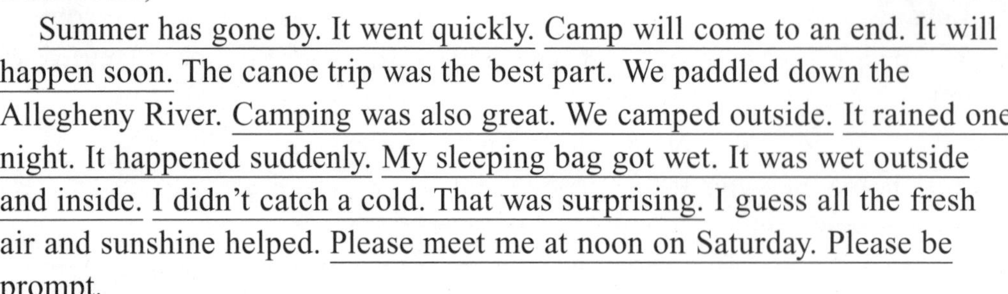

Dear Folks,

Summer has gone by. It went quickly. Camp will come to an end. It will happen soon. The canoe trip was the best part. We paddled down the Allegheny River. Camping was also great. We camped outside. It rained one night. It happened suddenly. My sleeping bag got wet. It was wet outside and inside. I didn't catch a cold. That was surprising. I guess all the fresh air and sunshine helped. Please meet me at noon on Saturday. Please be prompt.

Love,
Tommy

____

____

____

____

____

____

____

____

____

____

Grade 5: Unit 7 Adverbs and Prepositions *(Use with pupil book pages 248–249.)*
Skill: Students will combine sentences, using adverbs.

Name ___________________________

2 Comparing with Adverbs

Adverb	Comparing Two	Comparing Three or More
close	clos**er**	clos**est**
early	earl**ier**	earl**iest**
swiftly	**more** swiftly	**most** swiftly

A Write the correct form of the adverb in parentheses to complete each sentence.

1. Tala lives ______________ to school than Ali does. **(close)**
2. She arrived at the auditorium ______________ than Ali did. **(early)**
3. The final speaker spoke ______________ than the others. **(long)**
4. She spoke ______________ of all about monkeys and apes. **(earnestly)**
5. Chimpanzees resemble gorillas ______________ of all the apes. **(closely)**
6. Chimpanzees learn ______________ of all the apes. **(quickly)**

B **7–10.** This part of a student's brochure has four errors in comparing with adverbs. Use proofreading marks to correct the adverb forms.

Example: Gorillas learn more ~~easy~~ ^**easily** than you think.

Proofreading Marks
- ¶ Indent
- ∧ Add
- Delete
- ≡ Capital letter
- / Small letter

Proofreading

Help Raise Money for the Gorilla Project

The Gorilla Project studies gorillas intenselier than any other organization in the world. Its goal is to develop the most great understanding of the species. We are eagerly collecting funds for this group because we believe it is one of the most important organizations we can help. Trainers spend years teaching sign language to some gorillas. These gorillas have been most carefully taught than many children. It can be more hard to teach gorillas sign language than to teach people sign language.

(continued)

Name ______________________________

2 Comparing with Adverbs (continued from page 123)

Challenge

Read the chart to discover some interesting facts about certain kinds of animals. Then write adverbs that compare to complete the sentences below.

Animals that jump high	thoroughbred horse	8 feet	puma	23 feet
	hare	7 feet	impala	10 feet
	cat	6 feet	tiger	13 feet
Animals that have a long life span	Madagascar tortoise	200 years	chimpanzee	51 years
	Asian elephant	69 years	raven	69 years
	Pearl mussel	100 years	lobster	50 years
Animals that run fast	cheetah	71 mph	zebra	40 mph
	giraffe	31 mph	lion	50 mph
	camel	10 mph	hare	45 mph
Animals that move slowly	garden snail	17 feet per hour		
	sloth	5 feet per hour		
	red slug	6 feet per hour		

1. Of all the animals, the cheetah runs ______________.
2. Of all the animals, the sloth moves ______________.
3. The hare can jump ______________ than the cat.
4. Of all the animals, the Madagascar tortoise lives ______________.
5. The zebra moves ______________ than the hare.
6. Of all the animals, the puma can jump ______________.
7. The Asian elephant lives ______________ than the chimpanzee.
8. The red slug moves ______________ than the sloth.

Writing Application: A Report

You are a zookeeper. Write a comparison of some of the animals in your zoo. Compare and contrast the habits and personalities of at least three of the animals. Include an adverb that compares in each sentence.

Name ______________________________

3 Adjective or Adverb?

Adjectives	Adverbs
Jeanette Rankin was **confident**.	She spoke **confidently**.
She felt **well**.	She expressed herself **well**.
She did a **good** job.	She did her job **well**.

A Underline the correct word in parentheses to complete each sentence. Then write *adjective* or *adverb* for each underlined word.

1. April 6, 1917, was (special, specially). __________
2. Would the important vote in Congress go (good, well)? __________
3. Most politicians supported the war (firm, firmly). __________
4. Jeanette Rankin thought war was (wrong, wrongly). __________
5. She believed (strong, strongly) in peace. __________
6. She expressed her opinion (good, well.) __________

B **7–12.** This news story has six incorrectly used adjectives or adverbs. Use proofreading marks to correct the news story.

Example: Jeannette Rankin spoke ~~quiet~~ **quietly** but forcefully.

Proofreading Marks

- ¶ Indent
- ∧ Add
- Delete
- ≡ Capital letter
- / Small letter

Rankin Votes No!

Today, Jeanette Rankin, the first woman in Congress, spoke clear. She was definitely in her vote against U.S. entry into World War I. The vote was quickly, and it was obviously that Jeanette's side lost. Her decision against the war had been difficult. Jeanette had offended many people. After the vote, people did not treat her good. Many people, however, thought she had acted courageous.

(continued)

Name ____________________

3 Adjective or Adverb? *(continued from page 125)*

Challenge

The last names of some courageous people are hidden in the sentences below. Circle each last name, and write the full name on the line. Then complete each pair of sentences. Write an adjective to complete the first sentence. Then complete the second sentence with an adverb that is made by adding *-ly* to the adjective.

Example: Rosa was tired from walking all the way from the park, so she sat in the first seat she could find on the bus. **Rosa Parks**

Rosa was **courageous**. She worked **courageously** for civil rights.

1. Paul warned the minutemen and forever enjoyed the respect of the colonists.

   ____

   The night was ________. He shouted ________.

2. Florence strode out at night in gales and rain to help the wounded soldiers.

   ____

   Her lamp was ________. It shone ________ in the night.

3. As Harriet waited for the signal, the slave was forced to hide behind the bathtub many hours. ____________________

   Harriet was ________. She fought ________ for freedom.

4. Neil held in his arm strong evidence that the United States was the first to land a person on the moon. ____________________

   Neil was ________. He stood ________ on the lunar surface.

Writing Application: A Biography

Write a short biography of a famous person or of someone you know who performed a courageous act or took an unpopular stand. Use three adjectives and three adverbs in your biography. Include *good* and *well.* Underline each adjective. Circle each adverb.

Grade 5: Unit 7 Adverbs and Prepositions *(Use with pupil book pages 252–253.)*
Skill: Students will use adjectives and adverbs correctly.

Name ________________________________

4 Negatives

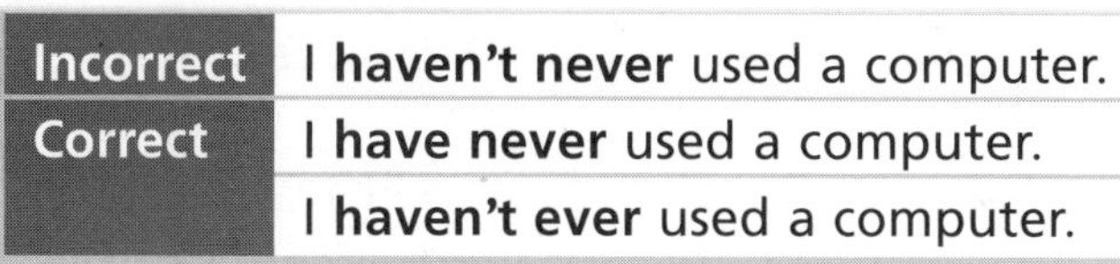

Incorrect	I **haven't never** used a computer.
Correct	I **have never** used a computer.
	I **haven't ever** used a computer.

A Rewrite each sentence, correcting the double negative.

1. I never used nothing so difficult.

   ____

2. I don't see no directions anywhere.

   ____

3. Won't nobody help me?

   ____

4. No one never plugged in the computer.

   ____

B **5–8.** Use proofreading marks to correct four double negatives in this computer checklist.

Example: The problem is that no one ~~never~~ ^ever taught me how to work this crazy thing.

Proofreading Marks

- ¶ Indent
- ∧ Add
- ℘ Delete
- ≡ Capital letter
- / Small letter

Proofreading — e-mail

Rules for Using the Computer

- Save your work often or you won't have no good files.
- Nothing with magnets musn't go near the computer.
- Never eat nothing while you work on the computer.
- Beverages don't belong nowhere near the computer.
- Nobody should pick up or move the computer.

(continued)

Name ______________________________

4 Negatives *(continued from page 127)*

Challenge

Computer information is usually stored on small, flat disks. These disks are very sensitive and require special handling. The warning signs below show the things we should not do when we are working with computer disks. Write a sentence for each warning sign. Use one negative word in each sentence.

1. 

____

____

____

3. 

____

____

____

2. 

____

____

____

4. 

____

____

____

Writing Application: An Advertisement

Suppose you work for an advertising company. You must write an advertisement for a new computer. Use a negative in each sentence of your advertisement. Be sure that you do not use any double negatives.

Grade 5: Unit 7 Adverbs and Prepositions *(Use with pupil book pages 254–255.)*
Skill: Students will use negatives correctly in sentences.

Name ______________________________

5 Prepositions

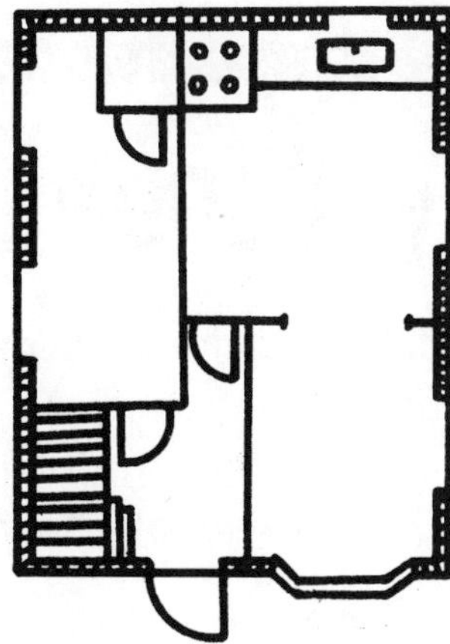

> preposition object
> The architect displayed the drawing **of** the house.
>
> preposition object
> She showed it **to** them.

Underline the preposition in each sentence. Then write the object of the preposition.

1. Harriet designs buildings of many types. ______________
2. She is working on several projects. ______________
3. Her office is inside this building. ______________
4. Blueprints are scattered across her desk. ______________
5. Her drafting table is under a skylight. ______________
6. A detailed model is by the window. ______________
7. Several miniature trees are around it. ______________
8. Harriet spends long hours in this office. ______________
9. However, she also goes to the construction site. ______________
10. She brings the blueprints with her. ______________
11. A supervisor meets her at the gate. ______________
12. Harriet walks through the structure. ______________
13. She checks below the ground level. ______________
14. She climbs up the ladder. ______________
15. The workers talk about the project. ______________
16. Problems are discussed during this meeting. ______________
17. These problems cannot wait until the last minute. ______________
18. The architect must find solutions for them. ______________

(continued)

Name ______________________________

5 Prepositions *(continued from page 129)*

Challenge

Below is an architect's plan for a new house. The new owners, Mr. and Mrs. Lang, want to see where their furniture will fit. You can help them with the arrangement by drawing the furniture where you think it should be placed. Use the symbols shown below for the furniture.

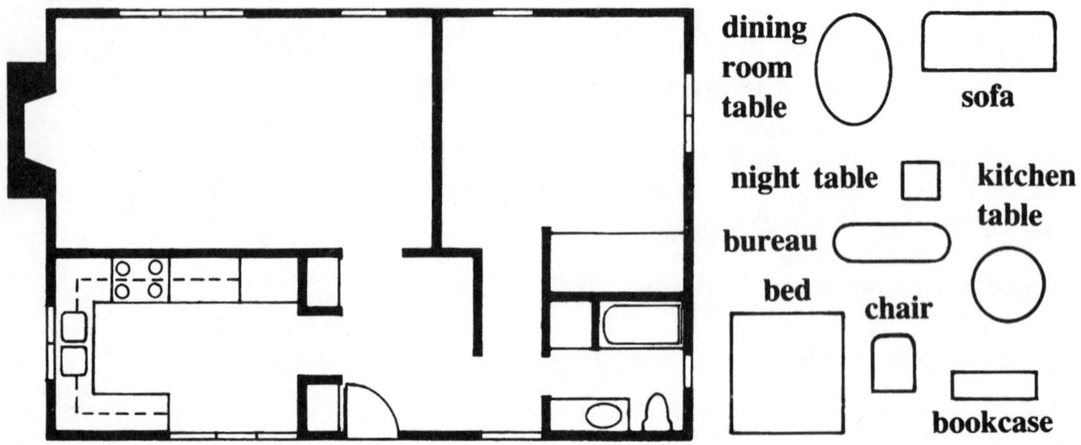

Now write a paragraph, describing your suggestions for the placement of the furniture. Use a preposition in each sentence. Underline each preposition once and the object of the preposition twice.

____

____

____

____

____

____

Writing Application: A Persuasive Letter

A new community center is being planned for your town. As an architect, you would like to design the building. Write a persuasive letter to the building committee, telling why you think your design is best. Include at least five prepositions in your letter. Underline the prepositions.

Grade 5: Unit 7 Adverbs and Prepositions *(Use with pupil book pages 256–257.)*
Skill: Students will use prepositions in sentences.

Name ______________________________

6 Prepositional Phrases

preposition object object
Mistakes **in construction** and **manufacturing** can be dangerous.
prepositional phrase

preposition object
Laws protect people **from** these **mistakes**.
prepositional phrase

Write the prepositional phrase in each sentence. Underline the preposition once and the object of the preposition twice.

1. The Tacoma Narrows Bridge in Washington opened in 1940.

____

2. The bridge was built across Puget Sound. ______________________________

3. At that time, it was the world's third largest suspension bridge.

____

4. Soon passengers inside cars and buses noticed that the bridge swayed.

____

5. After a few weeks, people began calling the bridge Galloping Gertie.

____

6. Crossing the bridge resembled a ride on a roller coaster or a boat.

____

7. During strong winds, the bridge swayed violently.

____

8. Officials finally closed the bridge to vehicles and people.

____

9. Eventually the deck fell into the water.

____

10. Now models of bridges must first be tested.

____

(continued)

Name ______________________________

6 Prepositional Phrases (continued from page 131)

Challenge

Below is a map of the town of Shambletown, which is in the state of Disrepair. Buster is anxious to get to the Fix-It Shop. Draw the route he should follow. He may not cross any broken bridges.

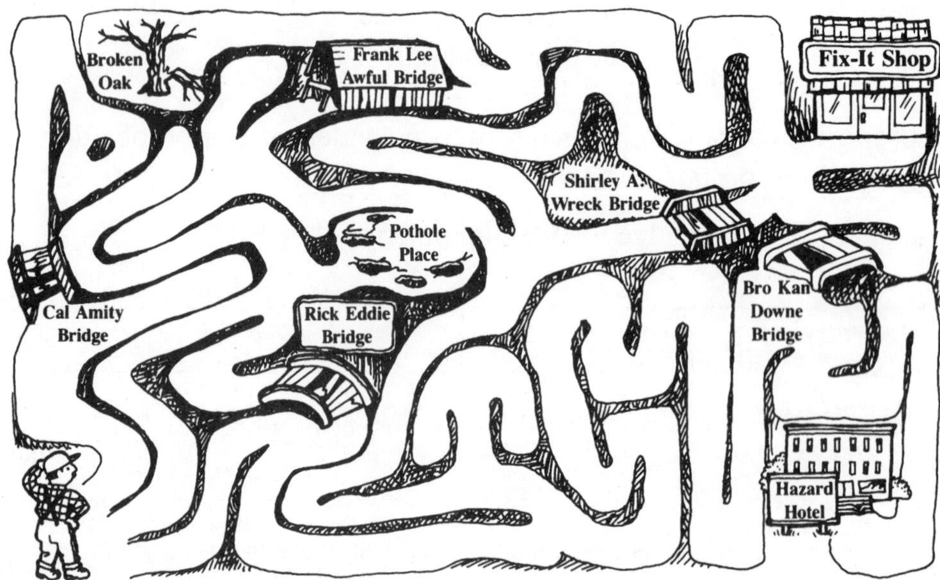

Now write directions, telling Buster how to reach the Fix–It Shop. Use a prepositional phrase in each sentence of your directions.

____

____

____

____

____

____

Writing Application: A Travel Journal

Think of an exciting or unusual trip that you have taken. Write a paragraph, describing that trip. Use at least five prepositional phrases in your description. Underline each prepositional phrase.

Grade 5: Unit 7 Adverbs and Prepositions *(Use with pupil book pages 258–259.)*
Skill: Students will use prepositional phrases in sentences.

Name ____________________

Writing with Prepositions

Sentence	I love to learn.
Elaborated sentence	I love to learn **about space**.
Incorrect	The first stop is Space Camp for a future astronaut.
Correct	The first stop **for a future astronaut** is Space Camp.

Elaborating Sentences: Prepositional Phrases 1–6. Rewrite these facts about a Space Shuttle. Add prepositional phrases to sentences that need more detail. Move prepositional phrases that are written in the wrong place. Use the picture for help.

Revising

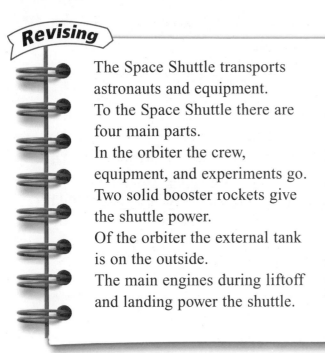

The Space Shuttle transports astronauts and equipment.
To the Space Shuttle there are four main parts.
In the orbiter the crew, equipment, and experiments go.
Two solid booster rockets give the shuttle power.
Of the orbiter the external tank is on the outside.
The main engines during liftoff and landing power the shuttle.

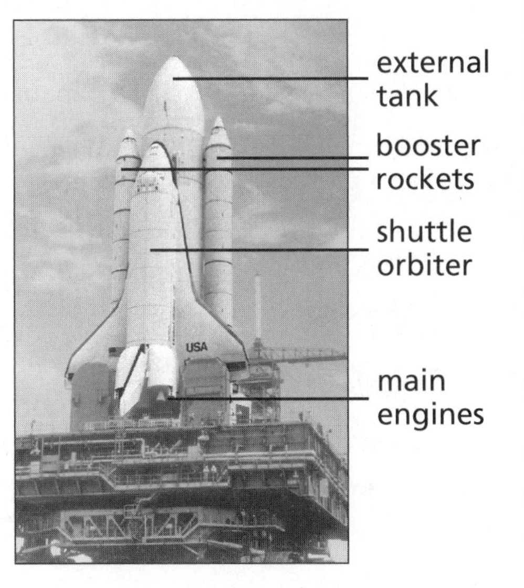

____

____

____

____

____

____

____

____

Name ____________________

Writing with Prepositions *(continued from page 133)*

Two sentences	The park is beautiful. The park is by the lake.
Combined sentence	The park **by the lake** is beautiful.

Combining Sentences: Prepositional Phrases 7–12. Rewrite this petition. Use prepositional phrases to combine each set of underlined sentences.

Revising

Save Our Park!

Our park is very important. It is important to our city. It is one of the city's finest features! Many people use the park. They use it for recreation. People like to walk through the park. They like to walk through it on their way to work. It is certainly more scenic than our city streets.

We do not need another high-rise apartment building. There is plenty of housing already. A high-rise would block people's views. They wouldn't be able to see the lake. Also a high-rise would bring hundreds. There would be hundreds of people and cars. This would cause congestion.

Please don't destroy our beautiful city park. Sign this petition. The city council will get it. They need to know how strongly we feel!

Name ______________________________

7 Pronouns in Prepositional Phrases

> The exercise teacher ran past **me**.
> I jogged after the other **students** and **him**.

A Rewrite each sentence, using the correct pronoun in parentheses. Then underline the prepositional phrase in the sentence that you wrote.

1. Exercise classes are held near (us, we).

   ____

2. Ms. Jay and Mr. Petrie usually arrive before my parents and (I, me).

   ____

3. From (her, she) and (him, he), we learn different exercises.

   ____

4. We always do warm-up exercises with the other students and (them, they).

   ____

B **5–8.** This part of a video script has four incorrect pronouns after prepositions. Use proofreading marks to correct them.

Example: No one in this class except Jason and ~~I~~ ^me can do sit-ups properly.

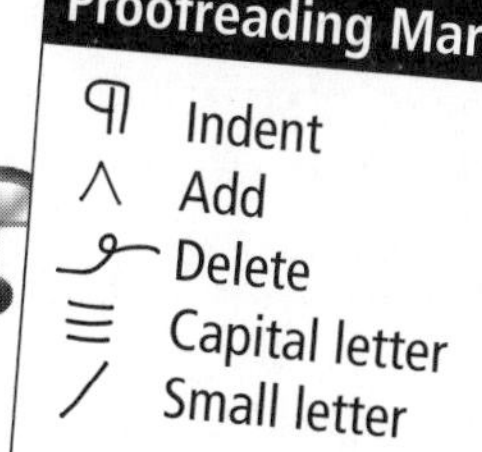

Instructor:

Are you ready to work out? Then come exercise with Sarah and I. Without we, you may have trouble. Follow along closely with we, and you'll be healthy.

These exercises are for you and they and everyone! Now let's get started! Sarah, show them how we stretch. Stretch everyone!

(continued)

Name ______________________________

7 Pronouns in Prepositional Phrases (continued from page 135)

Challenge

Read the first sentence in each pair below. Then write a prepositional phrase to complete the second sentence. The phrases you write are parts of common expressions. Each prepositional phrase should consist of a preposition and at least one pronoun.

1. Bo and Mo will learn crossovers. Just keep ____________________.
2. He just did one hundred pushups! I can't get ____________________!
3. Millicent just can't do knee bends. Stop picking ____________________.
4. Zeke and Joe are having trouble. Can we cover ____________________?
5. Si and Sophie need our support. Let's all get ____________________.
6. Sophie doesn't know her own ability. In fact, she runs rings ____________________ in weightlifting.
7. Sophie loves weightlifting. She's nuts ____________________.
8. Nella and I are learning to do leg lifts. Try to bear ____________________.
9. We know that the team can do better. Let's build a fire ____________________.
10. Mac tried to do fewer sit-ups, but he didn't get away ____________________.
11. Zoe and Mac think these classes are difficult. The classes are beginning to get ____________________.
12. Ava and he don't listen to the instructions. The teachers find it difficult to get through ____________________.

Writing Application: A List

EXPLAINING

Think of an activity that you and other students do in gym class. Write a list of sentences, explaining the steps involved in this activity. In each sentence, use a prepositional phrase with an object pronoun. Underline the prepositional phrases.

Grade 5: Unit 7 Adverbs and Prepositions *(Use with pupil book pages 262–263.)*
Skill: Students will write prepositional phrases with object pronouns.

Name ______________________________

8 Adverb or Preposition?

Adverb	The drawbridge moved **down**.
Preposition	The knight rode **down** the path.

If the sentence has an adverb, write the adverb. If it has a prepositional phrase, underline the prepositional phrase and write the preposition.

1. Several tourists mingled outside. ______________
2. More visitors waited inside. ______________
3. Hilary walked up the stairs. ______________
4. A knight in armor guarded the entrance. ______________
5. He put his helmet down. ______________
6. She passed by. ______________
7. She peered inside the darkened room. ______________
8. A guide invited her in. ______________
9. Hilary strolled around. ______________
10. Armor was displayed along all the walls. ______________
11. Hilary read the explanation above the armor. ______________
12. She looked up. ______________
13. Decorated shields dangled above. ______________
14. Heavy metal helmets hung below the shields. ______________
15. Hilary looked down a long hallway. ______________
16. Near the end was a jewel display. ______________
17. Hilary walked by the display. ______________
18. Shields had glittering jewels around their edges. ______________
19. Visitors heard noises above their heads. ______________
20. Hilary ran outside the building. ______________

(continued)

Name ____________________

8 Adverb or Preposition? *(continued from page 137)*

Challenge

Suppose you are a tour guide at an ancient castle. Each day you answer many questions from visitors. Using the picture below, write a sentence to answer each of the following questions. Use a word from the box in each sentence. Write your sentences on another piece of paper.

around	outside	over	up	down
inside	below	above	near	under

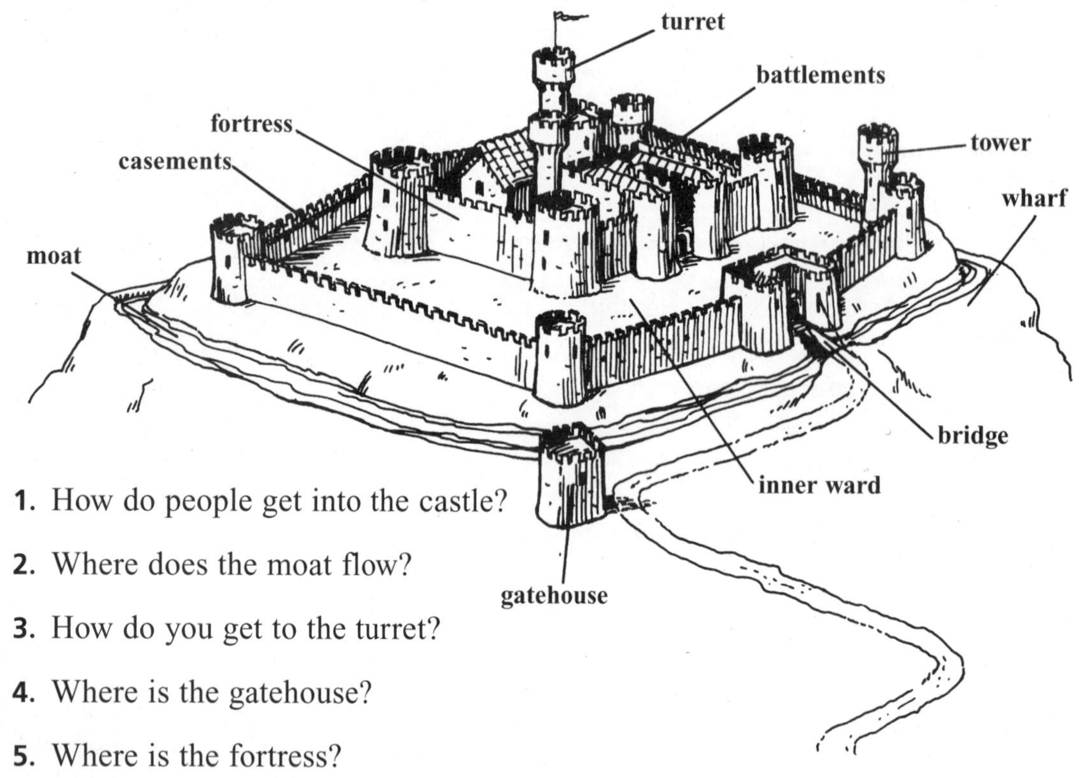

1. How do people get into the castle?
2. Where does the moat flow?
3. How do you get to the turret?
4. Where is the gatehouse?
5. Where is the fortress?
6. Can you see the moat from the tower?

Writing Application: A Speech

Suppose you are a museum guide in the year 2525. You are taking a group of students around a display of twentieth-century machines. Write a short speech, describing where you are walking and what is on exhibit in the museum. Use at least three adverbs and three prepositions in your speech.

Grade 5: Unit 7 Adverbs and Prepositions *(Use with pupil book pages 264–265.)*
Skill: Students will identify adverbs and prepositions in sentences.

Name ____________________

Choosing Different Adverbs

Lisa swung the baseball bat ~~slowly~~ powerfully.

1–10. Complete this sports report. Fill in each blank with an appropriate adverb from the box. Then compare your sports report with a partner's to see how using different adverbs can change the meaning.

respectfully	gradually	tightly	freely
wildly	nervously	similarly	suddenly
dully	invisibly	hardly	impatiently
unthinkingly	quietly	patiently	grandly
loosely	easily	happily	excitedly

Revising

When the team plays a home game, thousands pour __________ into the ballpark. Soon the stadium is packed _______. People stand _____________ for the national anthem. On the last note, the crowd roars _______. The first player steps up to bat and _______ makes a base hit. Then another player bats _________. The fans become restless, waiting ____________ for a big hit. Meanwhile, an announcer talks __________. __________, a crack rings out. Home run! The ball sails ________ out of the park.

Name ______________________________

Supporting Sentences

A **narrative paragraph** tells a story. It often has a lead sentence, supporting sentences, and a concluding sentence. **Supporting sentences** give details that support the main idea of the narrative paragraph. Supporting details help to answer *who, what, when, where, why,* and *how* questions about the main idea.

Complete the narrative paragraph about this picture. Read the lead sentence and concluding sentence below. Then write at least four supporting sentences, using details you see in the picture.

Why did I ever decide to be a pet-sitter? ______________________________

____

____

____

____

____

____

____

____

____

____

____

This is the hardest work I have ever done!

Skill: Students will complete a narrative paragraph with supporting sentences.

Name ______________________________

Organizing Your Narrative

The Day the Refrigerator Broke Down
2 milk tasted sour
~~my favorite is chocolate milk~~
3 had to throw everything away
1 not cold when door opened

Index cards listing events for a personal narrative about washing a dog are shown below. Read the details and sketch the event on each card. Cross out the card that has details that do not keep to the topic. Then number each remaining card 1, 2, or 3 to show the order in which the events happened.

time for my dog Fluffy's bath
I pushed her into tub.
___

my clothes soaked
water in shoes
___

Fluffy likes to ride in the car.
She's no trouble then.
___

lathered her up
She shook water and suds off!
___

Name ______________________________

Good Beginnings

Weak Beginning	Strong Beginnings		
	Surprising Statement	Question	Description
It was really cold and windy that day.	I thought I'd never be warm again.	Why in the world was I outside on a day like this?	The wind blowing off the lake was incredibly cold. Icy rain pelted my cheeks and nose.

Each short narrative below needs a beginning. Read the story. Then write two strong beginnings, using the strategies suggested.

1. . . . Mom pushed the wheelbarrow full of tulip bulbs, garden tools, and fertilizer to a small patch of garden. I helped her dig deep in the ground and carefully drop the bulbs into the holes. The bulbs we planted that day would hide underground all winter and send up beautiful flowers in the spring!

   Surprising statement: ______________________________

   ____

   ____

   Description: ______________________________

   ____

   ____

2. . . . My sister and I rushed outside, all bundled up in our warmest clothes. She flopped down to make a snow angel, and I started building a snowman. Who said it was too cold to play outdoors?

   Question: ______________________________

   ____

   ____

   Description: ______________________________

   ____

   ____

Grade 5: Unit 8 Personal Narrative *(Use with pupil book page 307.)*
Skill: Students will use different strategies to write strong beginnings for personal narratives.

Name ______________________

Writing with Voice

Weak Voice

I once again presented to my mother my objections to having to wear the revolting hand-me-downs of my older siblings. The clothes were all so unfashionable. Furthermore, they always had remainders of spilled foodstuffs.

Strong Voice

"Mom," I wailed, "why can't I ever have any new clothes of my own? These hand-me-downs are way out of style by the time they get to me. Besides, they always have drips and drops of everything all my brothers and sisters ever ate!"

The story below uses big words that sound unnatural. It lacks voice. Rewrite the narrative to make it sound like what you would say if you were telling the story.

My family set up camp in a clearing bordering the woods. That night, we heard a commotion in the brush. My brother was highly alarmed. I picked up the flashlight and directed its beam into the woods. In the light we saw a raccoon. We were relieved.

Name ________________________________

Good Endings

Weak Ending	Strong Ending
I finally crossed the finish line. I was so tired I barely managed to walk over to where my family was waiting.	Gasping for breath, I stumbled across the finish line, happy just to have finished. I limped over to my family. Maybe one day I would go out for the one-mile race again, but right now it hurt even to think about running.

Each short narrative below needs an ending. First, read the story. Then write two endings for it. Read your story endings and decide which one is stronger. Put a check mark in front of the stronger ending.

1. An opposing player ran toward me, kicking the soccer ball confidently in front of her. I licked my lips nervously and raced forward in an attempt to steal the ball. I closed in, stuck my foot out, and I had the ball! Now I just had to get it to the goal.

Ending: ____

____

____

Ending: ____

____

____

2. Why in the world had I ever agreed to sing a solo in the school chorus's concert? My turn to sing had come, and I felt totally alone on stage. I could see hundreds of eyes in the audience, all staring at me. I took a deep breath and opened my mouth.

Ending: ____

____

____

Ending: ____

____

____

Grade 5: Unit 8 Personal Narrative *(Use with pupil book page 309.)*
Skill: Students will write two endings for each narrative and then choose the stronger ending.

Name ______________________________

Revising a Personal Narrative

Have I **yes**

- written a new beginning that will grab my readers' attention? ❏
- added details that provide a clear picture of the events? ❏
- made sure the events are in order? ❏
- given the writing my own voice? ❏
- revised the ending to tie story ideas together? ❏

Revise the following narrative. Use the checklist above to help you. Check off each box when you have finished your revision. Use the spaces above each line, on the sides, and below the paragraph for your changes.

Going Sailing for the First Time

My dad asked me if I wanted to go sailing. He said it was a perfect day. The wind was just right for sailing. I told Dad I would like to go. Dad's boat is really pretty. If you saw it, you would know that it was designed to go fast. Dad pushed us away from the dock. I hoisted the mainsail, and it filled with wind. The boat sailed across the water, making little waves. Dad said to pull a little tighter on the sheet. That's the rope attached to the sail. I did, and the boat leaned to one side. I told Dad that I was scared, but he explained that we were just heeling. The boat moved very fast. It was very exciting!

Name ______________________________

Elaborating: Details

Few details	The first time I visited my cousins in the country, I was afraid of everything.
Elaborated with details	The first time I visited my cousins in the country, I was always looking over my shoulder, afraid of what might happen next. Even the chickens scared me!

The following paragraph is boring because it contains few details. Revise the paragraph, adding details to make it interesting for the reader.

Cleaning house is not my favorite thing to do, but I enjoy the time I spend with my dad each weekend. Together, we scrub the windows and run the vacuum cleaner over the floor. When we're finished, we collapse on the couch from working so hard.

____

____

____

____

____

____

____

____

____

____

____

____

____

____

____

Grade 5: Unit 8 Personal Narrative *(Use with pupil book page 312.)*
Skill: Students will revise a personal narrative, elaborating with interesting details.

Name ______________________________

Planning Characters

When you plan story **characters**, think about details such as how each character looks and speaks, and how each acts and feels. Also, think about the interests and personality each character has.

Think about a person, animal, or made-up creature that might make a good character for a story. Picture the character in your mind. Does he or she wear a funny hat? look confused? always speak in rhymes? Write details about the character on the lines in each category. Write something the character might say in the speech balloon. Then sketch a picture of your character.

Interests

____

____

____

Appearance

____

____

____

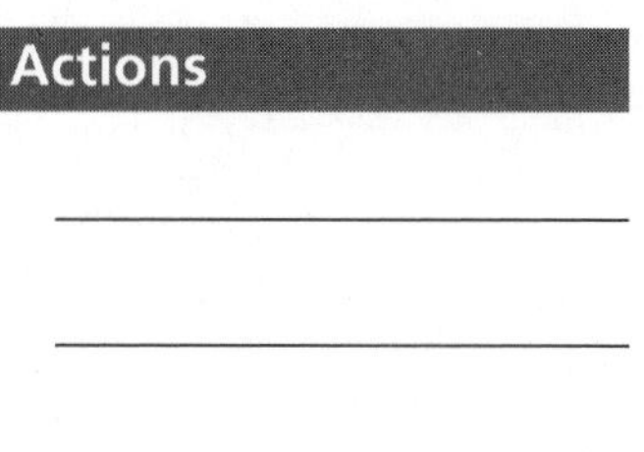

____

____

____

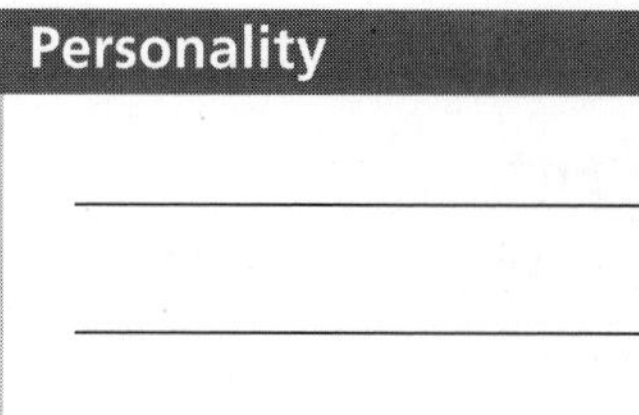

____

____

____

Feelings

____

____

____

Grade 5: Unit 9 Story *(Use with pupil book page 331.)*
Skill: Students will list details about a possible story character and then sketch a picture of that character.

Name ____________________

Planning Setting and Plot

The **plot** of a story has three main parts—the beginning, the middle, and the end. The **beginning** of a story introduces the **setting**, or where and when the story takes place. The beginning also introduces the main characters and the problem. The **middle** shows how characters deal with the problem. The **end** explains how the problem is resolved.

Think of a story you have read. Write a plot outline of the story in the story map below. Write only the main events for each part. Leave out the details.

Beginning: introduces the setting, main characters, and the problem	
Middle: shows how characters deal with the problem	
End: explains how the problem is resolved	

Grade 5: Unit 9 Story *(Use with pupil book page 332.)*
Skill: Students will complete a story map showing the plot outline of a story, including the main events of the beginning, the middle, and the end.

Name ____________________

Developing Characters

Here are three strategies you can use to make story characters seem more real.	
Include details.	The horse, an untamed and free-spirited filly, reared back on her hind legs, whinnied loudly, and fled like lightning over the hill.
Show actions.	Shawna took a deep breath, straightened her collar, smiled widely, and ran out to meet her new classmates.
Use dialogue.	"I hate hiking," grumbled Cara, "and I'm not sleeping in any cold tent with bugs for company either!"

Think about the character you sketched on page 147. Then write sentences about your character, using each strategy suggested.

1. **Details:** ____________________

2. **Actions:** ____________________

3. **Dialogue:** ____________________

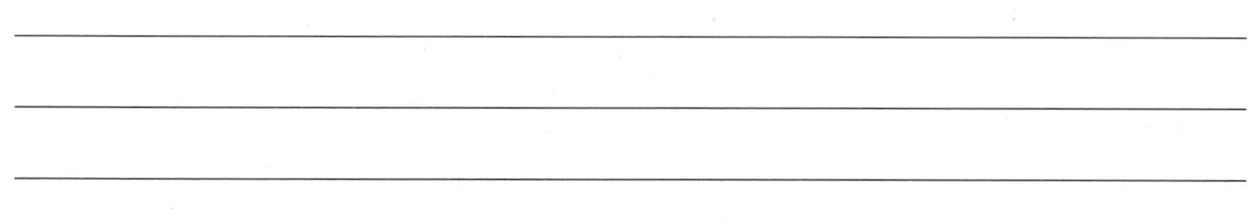

Name ___________________________

Developing Your Plot

The **plot** of a story has a beginning, a middle, and an ending. You can make the beginning of a story more interesting by describing the setting, describing an action, or using dialogue. You can make the ending of a story feel more complete by showing how the problem is solved or how the situation works out.

Read the middle part of the story below. Then write a beginning and an ending for the story. For the beginning, try describing the setting, describing an action, or writing dialogue. In the ending, show how the problem is solved or how the situation works out.

____

____

____

____

____

____

Instead, the family carried home a strange bird. He was a foot tall and had three fuzzy blue feathers on his head, a big orange beak, and green wings. They finally named him Harold. Harold could do many amazing tricks. He knew words in seven languages and could also turn on the computer with his beak.

Soon strange things began to happen. One of Eliot's friends said that someone with a shrill voice speaking Swedish had been answering the Halls' telephone. Then the police called. "Mr. Hall, your neighbors are complaining about loud music coming from your apartment during the day." Something had to be done.

____

____

____

____

____

Grade 5: Unit 9 Story *(Use with pupil book pages 334–335.)*
Skill: Students will write a beginning and an ending to go with the middle part of a story.

Name ______________________________

Writing with Voice

Funny	Suspenseful
Eric walked on-stage, carrying his saxophone. He was a little nervous but smiled widely. When he placed the mouthpiece in his mouth, he realized the reed was broken. Eric slowly turned, held his saxophone as if it were a guitar, and launched into a rousing rendition of "Hound Dog."	The eager audience applauded as Eric walked onto the stage. His warm, friendly smile put everyone at ease. Eric raised his saxophone and began to play. Suddenly Eric turned white as a cotton ball. Something was wrong, but what? Would Eric be able to play? What would he do?

The story below is dull and boring. It does not have voice. Rewrite the story, using voice. Try to create a mood that is interesting and entertaining. The mood can be spooky, silly, sad, serious, or any way you choose to make it sound.

An astronaut landed on a beach. It was early in the morning. She looked around but did not see any people. She tried to remember who she was, where she had been, and how she had gotten there. She could not. She began to walk along the beach. Then she saw a huge shiny dish that reminded her of the spacecraft she had been on. Her memory came back. She was home.

Name ______________________________

Revising a Story

Have I | **yes**

- developed a plot with a beginning, a middle, and an ending? ❑
- written an interesting beginning that introduces the characters, setting, and problem? ❑
- told how the characters deal with and solve the problem? ❑
- added details and dialogue? ❑

Revise the story below to make it better. Use the checklist above to help you. Check off each box when you have finished your revision. You may use the spaces between the lines, on the sides, and below the story for your changes.

The Case of the Missing Bicycle

Once upon a time, ten-year-old Detective Stevens was sitting in his messy office when a little boy burst through the door. He had a problem. He was very upset.

Detective Stevens calmed him down. He talked to the little boy. He listened very carefully. He took notes in a black book.

Then Detective Stevens looked for clues. He found some.

Then he found the bicycle in an old shack. James was happy. Detective Stevens was pleased.

He returned to his office happy he had solved another case.

Grade 5: Unit 9 Story *(Use with pupil book page 337.)*
Skill: Students will revise a story, using a revision checklist.

Name ______________________________

Elaborating: Details

Few details	Carley wrote her story, put it in an envelope, and mailed it.
Elaborated with details	Carley **neatly** wrote her story **in blue ink on plain white paper, carefully** put it in an envelope, and **immediately** mailed it **to the magazine editor**.

The following story is boring because it does not contain enough details. Revise the story. Use adverbs and prepositional phrases to add information to the sentences.

Maria and her friends wanted to start a computer club, but they did not have any computers. One day the club met. They needed computers, printers, and a scanner. They decided to ask people and businesses to help them. People donated lots of equipment. Many even donated their time and talents. The club was a great success.

____

____

____

____

____

____

____

____

____

____

____

____

____

____

____

Name ______________________________

Supporting Sentences

A paragraph that gives facts is called an **informational paragraph**. It has a topic sentence, supporting sentences, and a concluding sentence. **Supporting sentences** usually follow the topic sentence and give details that explain the main idea. Details can be facts, such as numbers, or they may be sensory words, which describe how something looks, sounds, smells, feels, or tastes.

Complete the informational paragraph about the picture. Read the topic sentence below. Then use what you see in the picture and the details provided to write four or five supporting sentences that explain the main idea in the topic sentence.

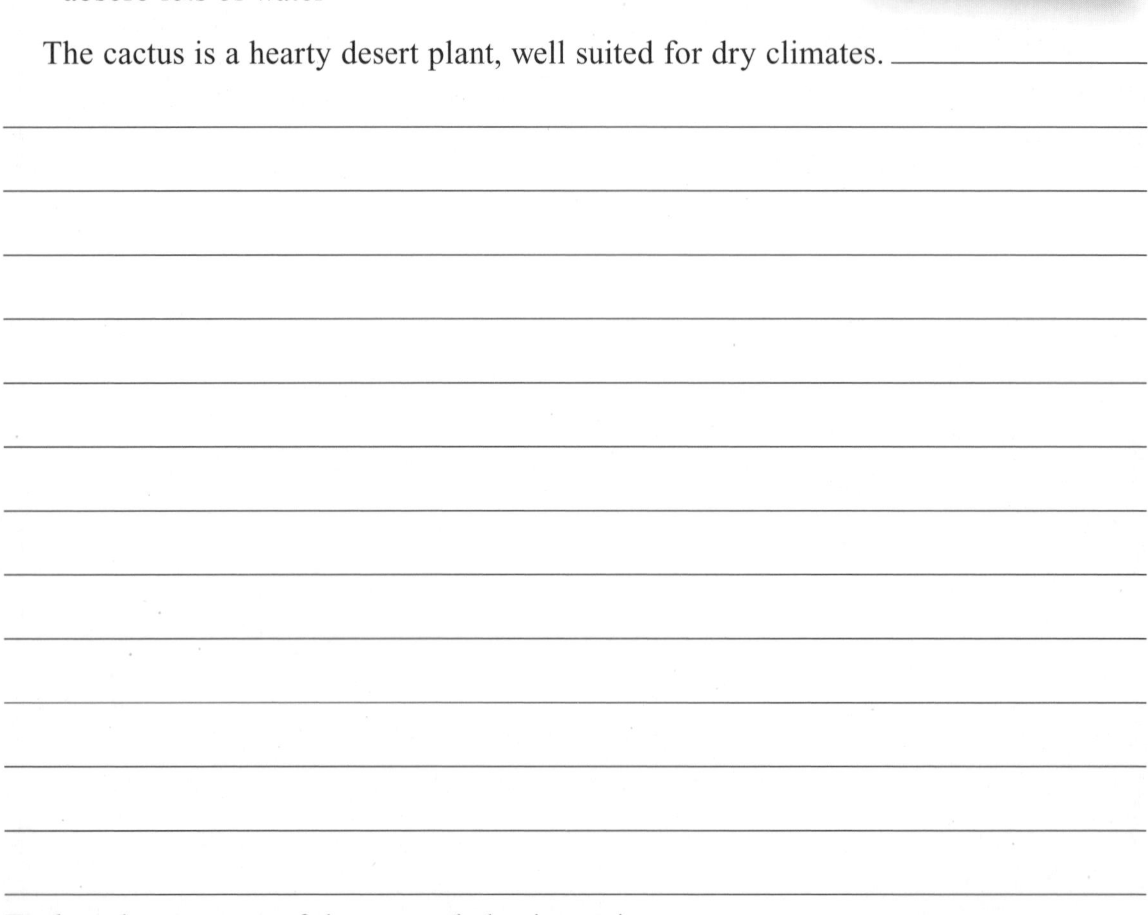

- Stem—thick, fleshy; stores water
- Skin—waxy; helps prevent evaporation of water
- Spines—long or short, soft or sharp; protect plant from being eaten by animals
- Roots—long, some up to 50 feet, or 15 meters; absorb lots of water

The cactus is a hearty desert plant, well suited for dry climates. ______________________________

____

____

____

____

____

____

____

____

____

____

____

____

____

Each and every part of the cactus helps it survive.

Name ______________________________

Organizing Your Essay

Feature	Mosquitoes	Spiders
appearance	brown, gray, black, or tan 6 hairy legs 2 eyes, 2 antennae	brown, gray, black, or tan 8 legs with sensitive bristles 2–8 eyes, no antennae
activity	can eat only liquids feed on plant juices females lay eggs some bite, spread disease	can eat only liquids trap insects in web for food females lay eggs few are harmful to humans

Use the information about newspapers and magazines from the Venn diagram to complete the chart below. Organize the details in feature-by-feature order.

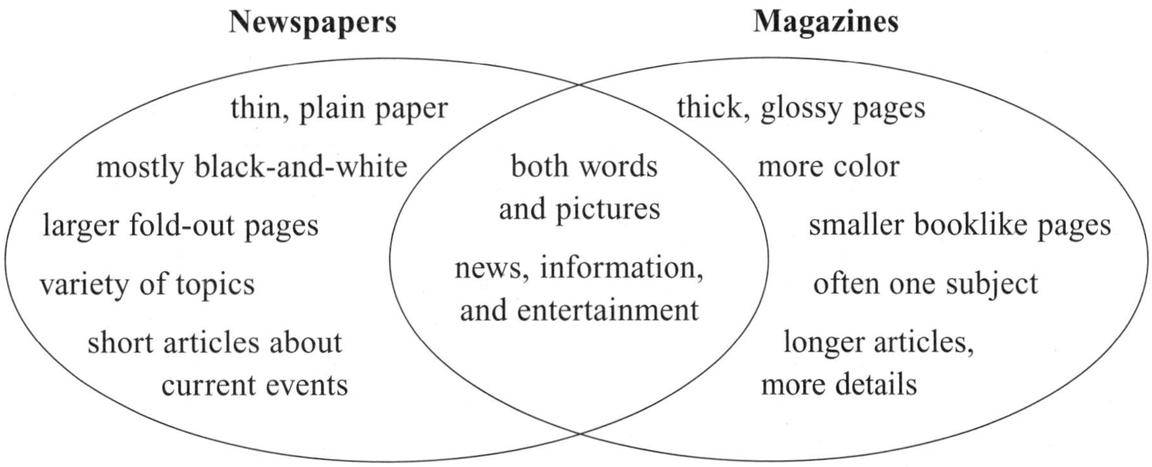

Newspapers **Magazines**

Newspapers:
thin, plain paper
mostly black-and-white
larger fold-out pages
variety of topics
short articles about current events

Both:
both words and pictures
news, information, and entertainment

Magazines:
thick, glossy pages
more color
smaller booklike pages
often one subject
longer articles, more details

Feature	Newspapers	Magazines
appearance		
purpose		

Name ______________________________

Introductions and Conclusions

Weak Introduction	Strong Introduction
Apples and bananas are different fruits, but they are alike in some ways.	Are you trying to choose between apples and bananas for a nutritious, delicious snack? Let's compare them.

Weak Conclusion	Strong Conclusion
Apples and bananas are both good to eat.	Whether you want a crisp, juicy treat or something soft and sweet, apples and bananas are nutritious, satisfying snacks.

The paragraphs below have a feature-by-feature organization that tells how apes and monkeys are similar and different. Read the essay. Then write a strong introduction and a conclusion that sums up the main ideas.

… Some similarities and differences help us tell them apart. Both are highly intelligent mammals. Apes live primarily in Africa and Asia, while monkeys live also in Central and South America. Monkeys eat just about anything, including flowers, fruit, leaves, insects, lizards, and eggs. Fruit and other plants are basic foods for apes.

Monkeys and apes are also different in appearance. Apes are generally bigger than monkeys. A gorilla, the largest ape, can be as tall as a human and can weigh up to 600 pounds. Monkeys' long arms and legs are really useful. Apes also rely on strong arms and legs. Unlike monkeys, however, most apes have arms that are longer than their legs. Monkeys use their long tails for balance as they move through the trees. Apes are excellent climbers, but they have no tails.

Introduction: ______________________________

____

____

____

Conclusion: ______________________________

____

____

____

____

Name ______________________________

Topic Sentences and Transitional Words

Both Chihuahuas and mastiffs are dogs, but they are not the least bit alike! First, look at their size. Mastiffs can weigh 185 pounds. On the other hand, the largest Chihuahua weighs only six pounds. Their heads and faces are different too. The mastiff has drooping ears and a squashed, sleepy-looking face, instead of the standing-up ears and pointed, alert face of the Chihuahua. How can two dogs be so different?

Each paragraph below needs a topic sentence and a few transitional words and phrases to help readers follow the ideas. Write a topic sentence for each paragraph, and add transitional words where they are needed in the paragraph.

1. … Both are powerful and can pull many tons of rail cars, but the diesel electric locomotive can pull more than the steam locomotive. The diesel electric does not consume as much fuel as the steam locomotive. The diesel electric does not produce nearly as much pollution as the steam locomotive.

Topic Sentence: ______________________________

____

____

2. … Both rabbits and hares usually have brownish fur to blend in with their surroundings. They both have large ears and eyes to detect predators. Hares are larger than rabbits and have longer hind legs. Their young differ in appearance. The young of the hare are born with fur and open eyes. The young of the rabbit are born without fur and are blind.

Topic Sentence: ______________________________

____

Name ______________________

Revising a Compare-Contrast Essay

Have I	yes
• written a new, attention-getting introduction that names my subjects?	❑
• compared and contrasted corresponding details for each subject?	❑
• included a topic sentence to state the main idea of each paragraph?	❑
• added transitional words and phrases to show connections?	❑
• revised the conclusion to sum up the main ideas?	❑

Revise the following compare-contrast essay to make it better. Use the checklist above to help you. Check off each box when you have finished your revision. You can use the spaces above the lines, along the sides, and below the paragraph for your changes.

Icebergs and glaciers are related. Both are made of ice, but they are very different in formation and size.

Glaciers form when snow does not melt. As new snow falls, it piles on top of the old snow. The ice gets so heavy it starts to slide very slowly downhill. Icebergs form when parts of a glacier break off and float free in the ocean. Glaciers are big. Glaciers can cover many square miles. The largest glacier, the ice of Antarctica, covers more than five million square miles! Icebergs are smaller. Most cover thousands of yards, but some are only a few square yards.

Name ____________________

Elaborating: Word Choice

Without antonyms	The tortoise is awkward and slow, but the cheetah is not.
Elaborated with antonyms	The tortoise is **awkward** and **slow**, but the cheetah is **graceful** and **quick**.

The following paragraph is not effective because the contrast between the two subjects is dull and wordy. Revise the paragraph, replacing the underlined words with antonyms that sharpen the contrast between the two subjects. Choose antonyms from the word list.

You might be surprised at the differences between rivers and lakes, the natural features that contain water. For starters, water in rivers moves along in a hurry, while water in lakes does not. The bottoms of rivers are not very smooth and rocky. Lake bottoms, on the other hand, are not rough and muddy. Rivers are usually not very far across, but lakes may be many miles across. Finally, rivers are usually not very deep, whereas most lakes, by comparison, are the opposite.

- rough
- narrow
- moves quickly
- shallow
- smooth
- deep
- stands still
- wide

Name ______________________________

Finding the Best Information

What I Know	What I Want to Learn	Possible Sources
Betsy Ross made the first U.S. flag.	Why did she make the flag?	*Betsy Ross: Designer of Our Flag* by Ann Weil
The U.S. flag has stripes and stars.	What do the stripes and stars stand for?	*World Book Encyclopedia*
The flag has changed over the years.	When was the last time the flag changed?	*The World Almanac for Kids, 2000*

Read the following K-W-S chart for a research report on Harriet Tubman. Then look at the sources listed in the box. Write the names of one or two sources that you think would provide the best information to answer each question. When you write, underline the titles you see in italics.

American Heritage Dictionary
atlas
biographical dictionary
Encyclopaedia Britannica Online
Fighters Against American Slavery by Stephen R. Lilley
Harriet and the Promised Land by Jacob Lawrence

What I Know	What I Want to Learn	Possible Sources
Harriet Tubman was called an abolitionist.	What is an abolitionist?	
H. Tubman helped slaves escape.	How did she help them escape?	
She took many slaves out of Maryland.	Where is Maryland?	
She was an African American woman.	Was she ever a slave herself?	
	Where was she born?	

Grade 5: Unit 11 Research Report *(Use with pupil book pages 412–413.)*
Skill: Students will choose reference sources to use to find particular types of information.

Name ______________________________

Writing from an Outline

Each main topic in an outline should have at least one paragraph. Each paragraph needs a topic sentence and supporting sentences for the details from the outline. Transitional words and phrases will help connect the ideas.

Write a research report paragraph from each of the partial outlines below. Remember to use transitional words.

Endangered Species

II. Giant panda
- **A.** Black and white bear-like animal
- **B.** Lives in the Himalayas
- **C.** Eats over 30 pounds of bamboo a day
- **D.** People cutting down bamboo forests to get land to farm
- **E.** Panda losing habitat

____

____

____

____

____

____

Great American Creators

I. Henry Ford, automobile maker
- **A.** Made his first car in shed behind home—1896
- **B.** Began Ford Motor Company—1903
- **C.** Developed method of mass production
- **D.** Produced first inexpensive car—Model T

____

____

____

____

____

____

Name ____________________

Introductions and Conclusions

Weak Introduction

Killer whales are mammals that live in the ocean.

Strong Introduction

Killer whales are more like human beings than you might think.

Weak Conclusion

By now, I am sure you can see how interesting killer whales can be.

Strong Conclusion

The next time you think of killer whales, picture them as mammals that live as a family, caring for one another.

Suppose you wrote a report on deserts from the following outline. Write two strong introductions and two strong conclusions.

Deserts

I. Description
   A. Regions with little water and vegetation
   B. Occupy over one fifth of the world's surface
   C. May be very hot or icy cold
II. Animals
   A. Adapted to desert life
   B. Come out at night when it is cooler
   C. Eat other animals or plants and seeds

Introduction: ____________________

____

____

Introduction: ____________________

____

____

Conclusion: ____________________

____

____

Conclusion: ____________________

____

____

Grade 5: Unit 11 Research Report *(Use with pupil book page 419.)*
Skill: Students will write two introductions and two conclusions for a research report.

Name ______________________________

Revising a Research Report

Have I | **yes**

- written a new topic sentence that presents the main idea in an interesting way? ❑
- added transitional words and phrases to connect ideas? ❑
- added facts from the outline to support the main idea? ❑
- revised the conclusion to sum up the important points? ❑

Revise the following research report paragraph to make it better. Use the checklist above and the outline section to help you. Check off each box when you have finished your revision. You can use the spaces above the lines, along the sides, and below the paragraph for your changes.

I. Black holes
   A. Stars with mass more than two times greater than the sun
   B. Heat pushes out, balances force of gravity when star burns
   C. No heat left to counteract force of gravity when star dies
   D. Mass of dead star squeezed into a single point—a black hole

Black Hole

A star of great mass becomes a black hole when it stops burning. When a star burns, its heat pushes out to balance the force of gravity. When it stops, no heat is left to counteract the force of gravity. Then the star is squeezed into a single point. This point is known as a black hole, because no light comes from it.

Name ______________________________

Elaborating: Word Choice

Without a definition	The Jefferson Memorial is on the banks of the Tidal Basin.
With a definition	The Jefferson Memorial is on the banks of the Tidal Basin, which is a large pool created to control flooding from the Potomac River's rise and fall with the tides.

The following paragraphs from a research report on Thomas Jefferson and the Jefferson Memorial contain words that might be unfamiliar. Revise the paragraphs, adding definitions from the glossary box to help readers understand. You can include the definitions within a sentence or add a new sentence.

Glossary	
architect	a person who designs buildings
portico	a porch
shrine	a place that honors the memory of a person or event
statesman	one who is wise in the business of government

A Memorial to a Great Man

The Jefferson Memorial, a shrine to Thomas Jefferson, is in Washington, D.C. It is circular, with a portico that has twelve columns. A statue of Jefferson stands inside.

Jefferson was the third President of the United States and a skillful statesman. Jefferson wrote the Declaration of Independence. He was also an inventor and an architect. It is no surprise that a memorial is dedicated to this amazing man.

____

____

____

____

____

____

____

____

____

____

Name ______________________________

Supporting Sentences

A paragraph that tells what someone thinks, feels, or believes is called an **opinion paragraph**. It often has an opinion statement, supporting sentences, and a concluding sentence. **Supporting sentences** support the main idea by giving reasons for the writer's opinion. Each reason is supported by details, such as facts and examples.

Write an opinion paragraph about your favorite season. Use the pictures shown below or your own ideas. First, read and complete the opinion statement below. Then write three sentences with details that give reasons to support your statement. Try to use at least one transitional word or phrase to link your sentences.

______________ is the best season of the year. ______________

____

____

____

____

____

____

____

____

____

____

Can you see why I like ______________ so much?

Name ______________________________

Elaborating Your Reasons

Opinion: The Family Fun Fair is a great event.

Reason	Details	Expanded Details
enjoyable activities	**examples:** rides, games	bumper cars, roller coasters, ball toss, bingo
good food	**fact:** Families bring homemade ethnic foods.	Chinese egg rolls, Mexican tacos, American hot dogs

Read the opinion statement and reasons in the idea pyramid below. Then write details, such as facts or examples, that support each reason.

Opinion: It is better to live in the country than in the city.

Reason: It is more peaceful and quiet in the country.	**Reason:** You can get closer to nature in the country.	**Reason:** You might feel safer in the country.

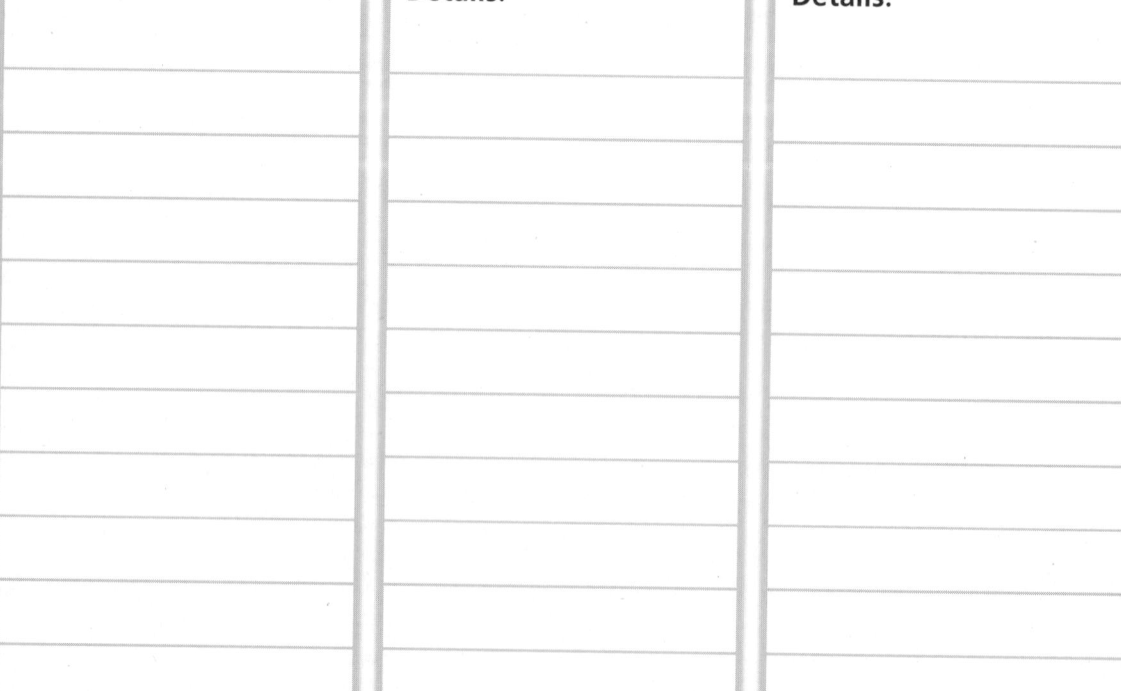

Name ______________________________

Organizing Your Reasons

Opinion: Participating in team sports is worthwhile.
2 It also helps you learn how to play well with others.
1 It provides opportunities to improve your athletic skills.
~~Practices can be tiring~~.
3 It helps foster good sportsmanship.

Read the opinion, the reasons, and the details in the pyramid below. Cross out the reason that is not supported with clear details. Write another reason and supporting details below the pyramid. Then number the reasons in the order you would write about them.

Opinion: The front hall is the perfect place for a student art display.

____ **Reason:** Lots of people would see the display.	____ **Reason:** There is a lot of space in the hall.	____ **Reason:** Everyone likes kids' art.	____ **Reason:** It would give visitors a good first impression.
Details: parents, kids, visitors	**Details:** wall space for pictures, space for tables to display 3-D art	**Details:** My mother likes my drawings.	**Details:** showcase students' talents, enhance appearance of the hall

____ **Reason:** ______________________________

Details: ______________________________

____

____

____

____

____

Name ________________________________

Introductions and Conclusions

Weak Introduction	Strong Introductions		
	Lively Opinion Statement	Question	Description
Everyone should have a bird feeder.	There's never a dull moment outside our kitchen window. Birds of all kinds are constantly nibbling at our bird feeder.	What's more entertaining than a movie? The birds at our bird feeder are, and you don't have to pay a cent!	Finches swoop down for a quick snack. Vibrant cardinals feast on lunch. There's constant motion at our bird feeder.

Weak Conclusion	Strong Conclusion
A bird feeder is fun. You should get one.	You'll soon be a big fan of bird watching. You won't believe how much you'll enjoy the sights outside.

Read the opinion essay paragraph below. Choose two strategies from above to write two interesting introductions. Then write two strong conclusions. Put a check mark in front of the introduction and the conclusion you like better.

Introduction: ________________________________

____

Introduction: ________________________________

____

… To begin with, it's a great relief to get away from my noisy family and have time to think. In addition, losing myself in an exciting book without being interrupted is something I treasure. Finally, having an hour to spend on a hobby without my whiny brother breathing down my neck is great.

Conclusion: ________________________________

____

Conclusion: ________________________________

____

Grade 5: Unit 12 Opinion *(Use with pupil book page 460.)*
Skill: Students will write strong introductions and conclusions for an opinion essay.

Name ____________________

Revising an Opinion Essay

Have I — **yes**

- written a new introduction that states my opinion in an interesting way? ❑
- added details, such as facts and examples, to elaborate my reasons? ❑
- put my reasons in a clear order of importance? ❑
- revised the conclusion to sum up important points? ❑

Revise the following opinion essay to make it better. Use the checklist above to help you. Check off each box when you have finished your revision. You can use the spaces above the lines, on the sides, and below the paragraph for your changes.

My Cute Pet

My kitten Sasha is the cutest pet in our neighborhood. First, she is cute to look at. She looks like a mop with eyes. Her pink nose and stubby whiskers just add to her charm. Her fur shines after she has been bathed and brushed. Sasha is cute when she plays. I can't stop laughing when she gets herself tangled in a ball of yarn. It's also fun to watch her pounce on her toy mouse. Sasha is cute when she sleeps. She finds a sunny spot, curls up in a ball, and drifts off to dreamland. For all these reasons, I think my kitten is the cutest.

Name ______________________________

Elaborating: Word Choice

Without synonyms	I **like** hiking. The fresh air is **nice.** The views from the hilltops are **pretty.** Hiking is **good** exercise.
Elaborated with synonyms	I **enjoy** hiking. The fresh air is **invigorating**. The views from the hilltops are **breathtaking**. Hiking is **wonderful** exercise.

The following opinion essay is not very interesting. It needs more exact language. Revise the essay by replacing some of the words with synonyms to make it more colorful.

Popcorn is a nice snack. First, it is easy to make. Put it in the microwave, and you'll have a good snack in minutes. It's good for you too. Popcorn also tastes fine. I love eating good popcorn.

Grade 5: Unit 12 Opinion *(Use with pupil book page 463.)*
Skill: Students will revise an opinion essay, elaborating with synonyms.

Name ______________________________

Supporting Your Goal

Goal: persuade my parents that I need a new bike
Reason: It isn't safe to ride my old bike.

Weak Support	Strong Support
Opinion: Other people might not see me at night.	**Fact:** The reflectors are broken.
Opinion: Fixing the chain all the time is a pain.	**Example:** I saw a boy have an accident when the chain fell off his bike.

Read the goal below and complete the web. Support the goal with reasons. Then write facts or examples that support each reason.

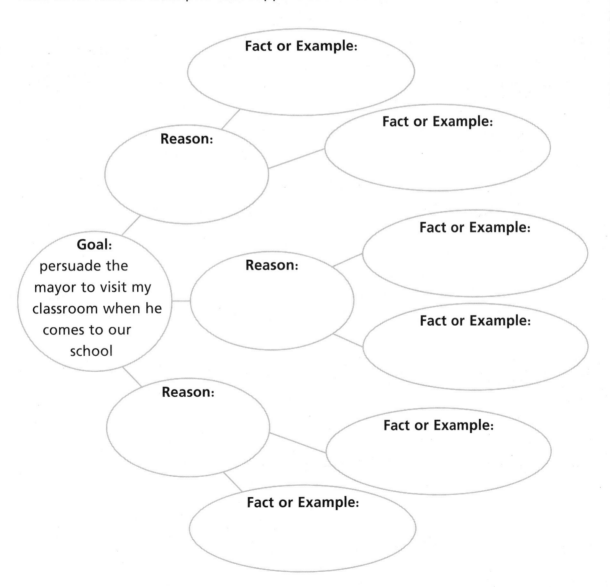

Fact or Example:

Fact or Example:

Reason:

Fact or Example:

Goal: persuade the mayor to visit my classroom when he comes to our school

Reason:

Fact or Example:

Reason:

Fact or Example:

Fact or Example:

Name ______________________________

Evaluating Your Reasons

Goal: persuade my parents that I need a new bike

Weak: Not an Accurate Reason	Strong: Accurate Reason
No ten-year-old rides a bike this small.	I am too big for my bike. My knees knock into the handlebar, even though I raised the seat.

Goal: persuade a business to sponsor our sports team

Reason for Business	Reason for Team
It's good advertising. People will see your name on our shirts and shop at your store.	The business will provide shirts for our team, so we'll have uniforms. Their money will also help pay for equipment.

Cross out the reasons below that do not have strong support or would not matter to the audience. Then fill in the web below.

Goal: persuade my parents to buy a computer

Reasons	Fact or Example
use for school projects	papers; the Internet
provide family entertainment	e-mail; games
everybody has one	neighbors; relatives
do better in school	writing; science
simplify life	save trips to the library; save time

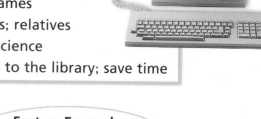

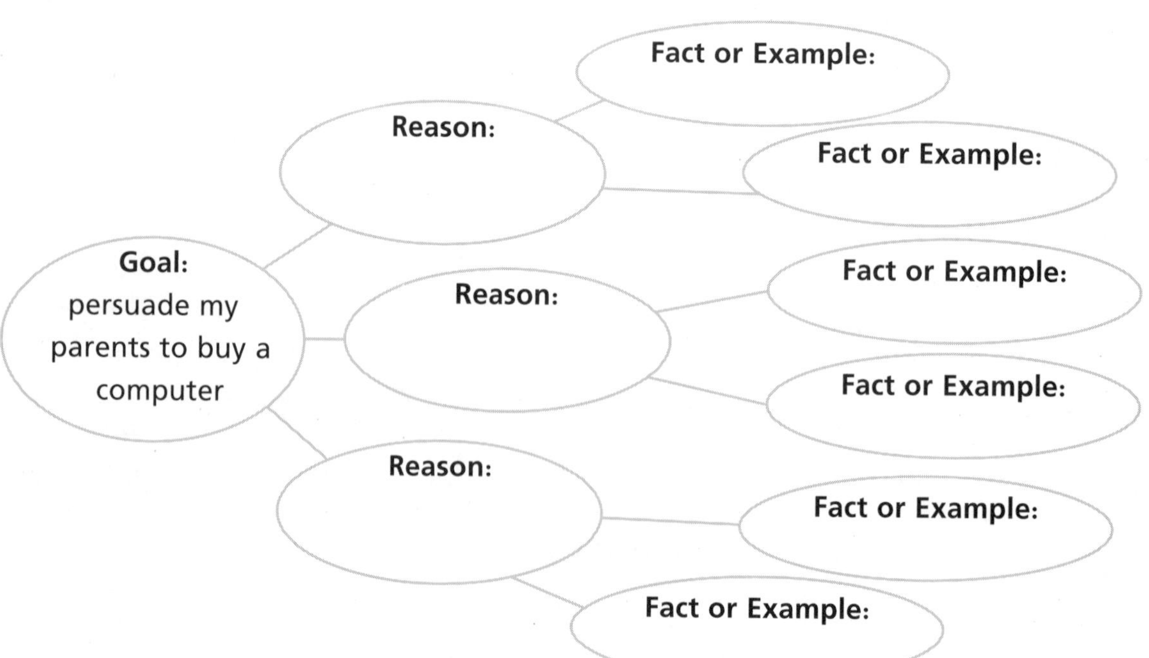

Grade 5: Unit 13 Persuasion *(Use with pupil book page 492.)*
Skill: Students will identify strong reasons to support a goal.

Name ______________________________

Organizing Your Essay

A well-organized essay tells reasons from most important to least important to get readers' attention, or from least to most important to build interest. It does not include reasons, facts, and examples that do not support the goal.

The web below shows reasons, facts, and examples that support a goal. Cross out the facts or examples that do not support the reason. Then number each reason 1, 2, or 3 to show the order in which you would write about them.

Goal: persuade principal to schedule gym for every student every day

____ **Reason:** Exercise is important.

- **Fact or Example:** helps you get along with others
- **Fact or Example:** keeps heart and lungs healthy
- **Fact or Example:** builds strong muscles and bones

____ **Reason:** valuable break in school day

- **Fact or Example:** get to move around
- **Fact or Example:** don't have to be quiet

____ **Reason:** improve athletic skills

- **Fact or Example:** running and jumping
- **Fact or Example:** eye-hand coordination
- **Fact or Example:** fun to play games

Name ______________________________

Introductions and Conclusions

Weak Introduction

It's important to know how to ride your bike safely. Our school should have a class in bike safety.

Strong Introduction

You're coming to an intersection. There is a car behind you. Do you know what to do? A bike safety course will teach you.

Weak Conclusion

That's why everyone should learn to play an instrument. Besides, it's fun.

Strong Conclusion

Playing an instrument will help you meet new kids, gain self-confidence, and do better in school. You won't regret signing up for the band.

Write two strong introductions for each goal below. Put a check mark next to the one you like better.

Goal: persuade city officials to build a community center for kids

Introduction: ______________________________

____

Introduction: ______________________________

____

Goal: persuade your parents to let you get a ferret

Introduction: ______________________________

____

Introduction: ______________________________

____

Goal: persuade a friend to read your favorite book

Introduction: ______________________________

____

Introduction: ______________________________

____

Name ______________________________

Writing with Voice

Weak: Negative Voice

A sack lunch every day is really boring. All I ever have is a soggy sandwich. Can't our school have a hot lunch program?

Strong: Positive Voice

By noon, I'm starving! I need something nutritious and delicious. A hot lunch program is the answer.

Weak: Not a Confident Voice

You should let me take care of my little brother. I think I'm old enough, and I'm usually responsible. This might be a good time to let me start baby-sitting.

Strong: Confident Voice

Please let me take care of Jared. You know I'm responsible, and you'll be nearby if I need you. I'll be the best baby sitter you ever had!

The essay below is not very persuasive. Suppose that you want to persuade your teacher to let fifth-graders use calculators for math tests. Rewrite the essay, using a confident voice. Add reasons and details. Then add a conclusion that sums up your goal and your reasons.

I think fifth-grade students should be allowed to use calculators during math tests. To begin with, we would probably do a better job on our tests. Also, we might be able to get more problems done during the time allotted. Finally, since older kids get to use calculators, I think that we should too.

Name ____________________

Revising a Persuasive Essay

Have I | **yes**
- written an introduction that states the goal in a lively way? ❑
- stated reasons that support the goal and put them in a clear order? ❑
- added details, such as facts and examples, that back up the reasons? ❑
- given the writing a voice that is confident and persuasive? ❑
- revised the conclusion to sum up the reasons and restate the goal? ❑

Revise the following persuasive paragraph to make it better. Use the checklist above to help you. Check off each box when you have finished your revision. You can use the spaces above the lines, on the sides, and below the paragraph for your changes.

Summer Vacation

You should let me spend the summer on Grandpa's ranch. For one reason, I could experience a different way of life. Since we live in the city, it would be good for me to see how other people live. I could also learn new things, like how to ride a horse. Most important, it would give me a chance to really get to know Grandpa and how he lives. He could tell me stories about what life was like when he was my age. Usually I get to see Grandpa only for a day or two when he's visiting us. I would have a great summer on Grandpa's ranch.

Name ______________________________

Elaborating: Details

Without details	Things at a water park would attract kids.
Elaborated with details	Giant water slides, towering diving boards, and inviting wave pools would attract kids of all ages to the water park.

The following essay isn't very persuasive because it doesn't contain enough details to support the reasons. Revise the essay, adding vivid, descriptive details to elaborate the reasons.

Our family should go to Rosie's for dinner tonight. Most important, Rosie's serves lots of different kinds of foods. Also, it isn't very expensive. In addition, it's close to home. Rosie's is my favorite place to eat!